ISAAC ASIMOV is undoubtedly America's foremost writer of science for the layman. An Associate Professor of Biochemistry at the Boston University School of Medicine, he is the author of such standards of science reportage as THE GENETIC CODE, THE UNIVERSE, FACT AND FANCY, and the three-volume UNDERSTANDING PHYSICS, in addition to many science fiction works considered classics in the field. Born in Russia, Isaac Asimov came to this country with his parents at the age of three, and grew up in Brooklyn. In 1948 he received his Ph.D. in Chemistry at Columbia and joined the faculty at Boston University. Jonathan N. Leonard, the Science Editor of Time, has called him that "rare phenomenon, a professional scientist [biochemist] who handles words skillfully."

## Also by Isaac Asimov

# FROM
## EARTH
## TO HEAVEN

Isaac Asimov

 DISCUS BOOKS/PUBLISHED BY AVON

All essays in this volume are reprinted from *The Magazine of Fantasy and Science Fiction*. Individual essays appeared in the following issues:

© 1964, 1965, 1966 by Mercury Press, Inc.

AVON BOOKS
A division of
The Hearst Corporation
959 Eighth Avenue
New York, New York 10019

Copyright © 1966 by Isaac Asimov.
Copyright © 1964, 1965, 1966 by Mercury Press, Inc.
Library of Congress Catalog Card Number: 66-20967.

First Printing (Discus Edition), July, 1972

DISCUS BOOKS TRADEMARK REG. U.S. PAT. OFF. AND
FOREIGN COUNTRIES, REGISTERED TRADEMARK—
HECHO EN CHICAGO, U.S.A.

Printed in the U.S.A.

To:
Lawrence P. Ashmead
and Celina S. De Lilla,
for bringing the warmth of friendship
to the editorial function.

# CONTENTS

# INTRODUCTION

AT THE BEGINNING of the last act of Shakespeare's *A Midsummer Night's Dream*, Theseus speaks with indulgent skepticism of the tale of enchantment related by the four lovers who had encountered fairies in the woods of Athens the night before. He says:

> The poet's eye, in a fine frenzy rolling,
> Doth glance from heaven to earth, from earth to heaven;
> And, as imagination bodies forth
> The forms of things unknown, the poet's pen
> Turns them to shapes, and gives to airy nothing
> A local habitation and a name.

The function of the poet, as here expressed, would certainly seem to be the very opposite of that of the scientist. The scientist, according to the popular stereotype, savagely eschews "the forms of things unknown" and will not deal with an "airy nothing."

He wants observations; he wants the turning of the needle against the dial, the blip on the oscilloscope, the color change in the solution, the granular darkening on the photograph. He wants something he can see, hear, smell, taste, or touch.

Having all that, he then reports it all with the careful excision of every last chemical trace of poetry. In dry, stilted phraseology, he describes exactly what he has found, interlarding every statement with a semiwithdrawal in the shape of a qualifying phrase, and then translating the whole into a grammatical construction peculiar to the scientific paper—the Impersonal Passive.*

This, I repeat, is the popular stereotype, but it is not always so.

Poetry wells up within all men and there are few indeed, even among the most inarticulate, who haven't at one time or another felt strange emotions stirring within them and crying out for utterance somehow.

Scientists feel it too; all the more so, since science deals with the very stuff of poetry.

Not all the soaring genius of Shakespeare, certainly the greatest poet who ever lived, sufficed to lift him to such empyrean heights as to reveal to him the vision of the universe that bursts in upon the dullest scientist who now lives.

The vision of science may go unappreciated, but it is there. It may be reduced by a plodding soul to mere dots on a photographic plate, or mere lines on a graph, but it is there. It may be drained of juice and pounded into flat phrases, but it is there.

And if none of us can communicate that vision with the sure touch of a Shakespeare, it is the privilege of every one of us to try if we choose. Even the most dismal failure can serve at least to sharpen the unexpressed and inexpressible wonder within the mind and soul of the man making the attempt.

Indeed, poetry is where you find it and, I myself find it often in statistics. I am not much of a traveler and I have virtually never seen a mountain tall enough to have a snow cover in summer, except in photographs. I get only the faintest whisper of the beauty and majesty of such a sight. But I compensate by finding beauty in the inanimate competition for the crown of "highest mountain in the world." I delight in deciding that there

*As an example of this inspiring form of writing, I give you the solemn phrase "It was earlier demonstrated by the investigator that—"Very few scientists are brave enough to dare write, "I once showed that—"

are three ways to define the height of a mountain, and that, by using each of these definitions in turn, three different mountains win the crown.

The distribution of fresh water among the lakes, and of land among the islands; the stretching northward and southward of the continents; all become a matter of fascination to me.

In every branch of science, similar fascinations lurk, ready to burst out upon even the most steadfastly resistant scientist.

Peeping from behind the symbols of the mathematician are formulas so beautiful in their symmetry that no artist could improve on them.

The thrill of unexpected discovery; the appearance of crystals in a mixture from which no crystals ought to have separated; cannot help but stir the blood.

The numberless array of atoms, expressed by zero after zero after zero, ends in a magnificent multiplicity that clarifies the universe, so that the unthinkable becomes an invaluable aid to thought.

And where, however fine the frenzy, can one come across forms of things not only so thoroughly unknown but so majestically unknowable as in the world within the atom. All the dictates of "common sense"—based upon the ordinary world about us—break down in the face of the ultimately tiny.

Imagine the poetry of a science that calmly abandons common sense in order to preserve sense; a science that admits into its fold an ineluctable uncertainty in order to be more nearly certain. What mysteries, what clanking chains, what dim ghosts of Gothic romance can compare with the mysterious muon-neutrino, whose tiny structure differs from that of the electron-neutrino, even though every last detail of the two tallies? Where is this definite difference that can nowhere be located? All science can do is give the particles a local habitation and a name—and hope for the best.

But nowhere does the poetry and grandeur of science

11

shine so inescapably and in so multifaceted a manner as in astronomy. The universe has grown beyond all recognition since Shakespeare's day, and the poet's eye in rolling from earth to heaven traverses not only the few miles that separates him from the clouds—but stretches upward through the trillions of miles that make up the light-year, and then through the billions of light-years that stretch out to a vague edge of a universe bounded by a speed of light that somehow seems tied into the very fabric of the cosmos.

The instruments of man are stretching out to that end and at the tip of their present reach lie the vague radiations that may represent the long-ago birth pangs of the universe, still bearing their message though ten billion years and more have passed since their weary journey began.

There is poetry everywhere and in everything, and it is most clearly present in the world that scientists have at their brain-tips. There remains only the task of expressing it, of casting it into the wind that it might be carried to all men.

Alas, that the poetic flame in me flickers so feebly— but for what light it can cast, I hold it up!

# PART I

## FROM EARTH —

# 1. OH, EAST IS WEST
# AND WEST IS EAST—

ABOUT HALF A YEAR AGO, I bought myself a sixteen-inch globe on a nice wooden stand, with an electric light inside and a brass holder to keep it tipped at twenty-three degrees. Now it stands in my attic study, to the left of my typewriter.

I use it as reference and as an objet d'art, but most often, I use it as a means of self-hypnosis. Faced with a nasty question as to just how to phrase some thought percolating through the softly reverberating interior of my skull, I can stare at the globe and find escape in a delightful period of non-thought as I study the outlines of Cambodia.

Of course, as a side effect, I am becoming more and more familiar with the shape of our planet's subdivisions, and I am beginning to fancy myself as a geography buff.

Consequently, you may imagine my chagrin when, faced with a simple geographic question, I came up with what I was told was a wrong answer. I have been fuming about it ever since.

Essentially, I was asked to name the American state which was farthest north, farthest south, farthest west, and farthest east, and you yourself are welcome now (without looking at a map) to write down your own opinions on the matter.

Have you done it? All right, then, I will now go into

the matter in detail and we'll see if I can't figure out some way of having been right all along.


Of the four cardinal points of the compass, north and south offer no problem at all. The turning of the Earth on its axis makes it possible for two unique points to exist on the planet; the two points where the axis intersects the Earth's surface. These are, of course, the North Pole and the South Pole. These can be defined in terms of latitude as 90.0°N and 90.0°S respectively.

We can define north then as the direction you face when you face the North Pole and have your back to the South Pole. Similarly, south is the direction you face when you face the South Pole and have your back to the North Pole.

These are absolute directions, too. If point B is north of A, there is no way of so altering your point of view so as to consider point B to be south of point A.

Let's take an actual case. The city of Omaha, Nebraska, is just about 1,000 miles nearly due north of Houston, Texas. Therefore, we would expect that if a person in Houston took a plane and flew 1,000 miles due north, he would end in Omaha.

Would our Houstonian, however, not also reach Omaha, eventually, if he flew south from Houston and continued flying in that direction without turning either left or right? And would not that mean that Omaha might be considered to be south of Houston?

The answer is no! Our traveler, flying south from Houston, would be facing the South Pole and after flying about 8,300 miles he would reach and pass over the South Pole. As soon as he had passed the South Pole, he would no longer be facing it. It would be at his back and he would be flying north. After flying north for 12,500 miles he would pass over the North Pole and promptly be flying south again. After traveling southward for 3,200 miles, he would reach Omaha.

All in all, he has traveled 12,500 miles north and

11,500 miles south. His net motion has been 1,000 miles north.

Therefore we need expect no confusion between north and south. We can answer such questions as: "Which is the most northerly state of the union?" without having to answer "Well, that depends—" We need only ascertain which state extends itself nearest the North Pole, and to determine that we can go by the parellels of latitude, which mark off the distance from the equator to the North Pole in ninety roughly equal units called "degrees." (They are not quite equal because the Earth is not quite a sphere.)

One trick to the question of "Which state" rests in the hope that the person being questioned will forget that the United States no longer consists of forty-eight states.

If the forty-eight states of "contiguous United States" are alone considered, then a hasty glance at the map may mislead you. In most drawings of the map of the United States, Maine, in the far northeast corner seems to be drawn so as to extend farther upward than Washington in the far northwest corner.

This is an illusion born of the fact that in most such maps, parallels of latitude are presented as curved lines, convex to the south. In a Mercator projection, in which the parallels are presented as perfectly straight and horizontal lines, you will have no trouble seeing that Maine falls short. Its most northerly point is only about 47.5° N, whereas the northwestern boundary of the United States is at 49.0°N.

If we concentrate on the Northwest, then and consider the perfectly straight line which marks off the boundary between the United States and Canada, we might be tempted to suppose there was no one most northerly state. Washington, Idaho, Montana, North Dakota, and Minnesota seem to be in a five-way tie at the 49.0°N mark.

This is not quite so, however, as you will find it you

inspect the northern boundary of Minnesota closely. The 49.0°N boundary continues eastward for about one-third of the way across the state until it reaches Lake of the Woods. It then turns abruptly northward for about thirty miles, chopping off a small section of the shore, north of the lake, before returning south to a line of rivers and lakes that carries the boundary gently southeastward to Lake Superior.

The section north of Lake of the Woods, about 124 square miles in area, is the northernmost portion of the forty-eight states, reaching about 49.4°N. The reason for the existence of this bite into what should clearly be Canadian territory, is the fact that in 1818, when that section of the boundary was established, maps were imperfect and the northern shore of Lake of the Woods was thought to be south of the 49.0°N mark. By the time the matter was straightened out, the United States had established sovereignty in the little jag under question, and Great Britain decided to let the matter rest.

It turns out, then, that Minnesota is, of the forty-eight states, the farthest north.

However, on January 3, 1959, Alaska was admitted into the Union as the forty-ninth state and a number of statistics had to be overhauled at once. As we all know, Texas had to be demoted to second-largest state, for Alaska, with an area of 571,065 square miles is 2.2 times as large as Texas. It is, indeed, nearly a fifth as large as all forty-eight states put together. (It is also larger than any Canadian province, larger even than Quebec, which has a land area of 523,860 square miles.)

In addition, Alaska carries off the palm as the nation's most northerly state. Every bit of it lies north of Minnesota's northernmost jag. Point Barrow, Alaska's northernmost point is, about 71.3°N.

Thanks to Alaska, the United States is one of the Arctic nations, but it is, nevertheless, far from being the most northerly. It is in point of fact, only fifth most northerly.

The fourth most northerly nation is Norway. Norway itself does not reach quite as far north as Point Barrow, but about five hundred miles north of that land is the island of Svalbard, better known to us as Spitsbergen. It is Norwegian territory and its northern tip reaches 80.8°N.

Third most northerly is the U.S.S.R. The northernmost point of Siberia (and of Asia, generally) is Cape Chelyuskin, which is roughly 77.5°N. Farther north still are a group of Soviet islands, collectively known as Severnaya Zemlya, which stretch north to about 81.3°N.

Second most northerly is Canada. Of Canada's mainland, the Boothia Peninsula stretches farthest north. Its northernmost point, at 71.4°N is the northernmost point of the North American mainland. In the Arctic Ocean, north of Canada, lies a group of islands under Canadian sovereignty. Most northerly of these islands is one called Ellesmere Island. Its northernmost point, Cape Columbia, reaches 82.7°N.

That leaves the most northerly nation of all and you might have some fun asking someone for a quick answer to "What nation is most northerly?" The answer is Denmark, which attains this distinction through its possession of Greenland. The most northerly point of Greenland, Cape Morris Jesup, reaches 83.7°N. It is the closest known land to the North Pole—which is only about four hundred miles farther north.

Now let's try south. The forty-eight states stretch southward in two places; in Texas and in Florida. The southernmost point in Texas is just southeast of the city of Brownsville, fifteen miles west of the mouth of the Rio Grande. There the state attains a latitude of 25.9°N.

Florida, however, does a trifle better. The southern

tip of the Florida Peninsula is at about 25.1°N. Running on a southwesterly line from southern Florida, moreover, are the Florida Keys, which curve down to a most southerly point at Key West, which is at 24.6°N. Florida is thus the most southerly of the forty-eight states.

Florida's distinction, like Minnesota's, was removed with the admission of a new state. On August 21, 1959, Hawaii was admitted to the Union as the fiftieth state.

The most southerly of the Hawaiian Islands is Hawaii itself. Its southernmost point, appropriately named "South Cape" is about 18.9°N, so that Hawaii is an easy winner for the title of most southerly state.

The fifty states of the Union, which spread over 52.6° of latitude from the Arctic Ocean to the tropical Pacific are nevertheless all in the Northern Hemisphere, so that the United States is nowhere in the running for the mark of the most southerly nation.

Of course, the most southerly land region of all is antarctica, on which the South Pole itself is located. However, Antarctica can scarcely be counted, for barring some transient scientists and explorers its population is zero.

If we eliminate Antarctica and the various scrubby islands off its shores, we could ask ourselves, "What populated nation is farthest south?"

We might begin by considering the three continents that extend south of the equator.

Of these, Africa does least well. Its southernmost point, Cape Agulhas (part of the Union of South Africa) is at 34.8°S. This is no closer to the South Pole than Los Angeles is to the North Pole, yet it suffices to make the Union of South Africa the fifth-closest nation to the South Pole.

Fourth closest is Australia. Its southernmost point, at Wilson's Promontory (southeast of Melbourne) is at 39.1°S. South of that point, however, is the Australian island of Tasmania, which reaches 43.6°S. This is about as close to the South Pole as Buffalo, New York, is to the North Pole.

New Zealand draws third place. It consists of two chief islands, North Island and South Island, and the southernmost point of the latter is at 46.6°S. In addition a small New Zealand island (Stewart Island) lies south of South Island and reaches 47.2°S, about as far south as Seattle, Washington, is north.

It is South America, however, that is the most southerly of the inhabited continents. It's shape, narrowing steadily, continues on for some five hundred miles beyond the most southerly point reached by New Zealand. Argentina and Chile, battling it out for first and second place, march down that southward stretch side by side, to the Strait of Magellan. Argentina stops short just before the strait, the entire shore of which is Chilean territory. The southernmost point of South America is therefore Chilean and is at 53.9°S.

To the southeast of the strait, however, is the island of Tierra del Fuego. Argentina skips over the strait and has in its possession part of that island. Indeed, the dividing line is north and south, with Argentina owning the eastern half and Chile the western. The southernmost part of the island is Argentinian at 55.0°S, but there are a few islands south of Tierra del Fuego that belong to Chile. The most southerly is Horn Island, on the south of which is Cape Horn, at about 56.0°S. Chile is therefore the most southerly nation and Argentina second.

Cape Horn, the most southerly land (outside Antarctica and surrounding islands) is, indeed, only 650 miles or so north of the northernmost tip of the White Continent. Even so it is no closer to the South Pole than Moscow is to the North.

We come, next, to east and west. At first thought, this should give us no difficulty. The east-west line lies

21

at right angles to the north-south line, and as you face north, east is at your right hand and west at your left. The existence of the North and South Poles thus completely defines east and west, as well as north and south.

In fact, east was probably the first direction to be distinguished by early man, since it was the general direction of the rising sun, and during the long cold winter nights, eyes must have peered eagerly in that direction for the first sight of dawn.

But there is no unique most-easterly or most-westerly point. This introduces a certain confusion.

For instance, both Quito, Ecuador, and the mouth of the Amazon River are on the equator. If you look at a map of South America, you will see that Quito is about 2,100 miles due west of the mouth of the Amazon. If you were at the mouth of the Amazon and flew 2,100 miles due west, you would reach Quito.

Of course, you could leave the mouth of the Amazon in an easterly direction and by traveling 22,900 miles reach Quito in that way, too.

This may look like our previous attempt to reach Omaha by traveling southward from Houston, but it isn't. In traveling southward from Houston, we changed our direction to northward when we crossed the South Pole, the unique most-southerly point. There is no unique most-easterly point, however, and in traveling east from the mouth of the Amazon, we can reach Quito without ever going in any direction *but* east. In fact, you could keep circling the earth forever, traveling eastward at all times. And, of course, the same goes for traveling westward.

Let's put it another way— You can travel due north or due south for no more than 12,500 miles; but you can travel due east or due west for an infinite distance. This means that we can't play the game of finding a most easterly nation or a most westerly nation. Europe is east of North America, but Asia is east of Europe and North America is east of Asia—and so on forever.

Well, then, what can we do about this mess? Shall we say that Quito is 2,100 miles west of the mouth of the Amazon? Or 22,900 miles east?

Surely, any sane man would say, "Choose the direction that gives you the smaller number!"

It is not always easy to tell which direction gives the smaller number, however, for the full length of the east-west direction varies with latitude. At the equator, you will travel due east (or west) 25,000 miles before returning to your starting point. At the latitude of Minneapolis, Minnesota, you will travel only 17,500 miles and at the latitude of Oslo, Norway, only 12,500 miles.

It would make sense therefore to say something is 10,000 miles east of Quito, but not 10,000 miles east of Oslo. In the latter case you should more properly say it is 2,500 miles west of Oslo.

To avoid this sort of ambiguity, we can make use of degrees of longitude. The earth is sliced into longitudinal degrees as an orange is sliced into segments, and every east-west journey covers exactly 360° in returning to the starting point. If, as one goes north (or south) from the equator, the total length of the east-west journey decreases, so, in exactly matching fashion, does the length of the longitudinal degree.

If we measure distances east and west in degrees, then, we can choose the direction that will give us a figure of less than 180° and that will remove all ambiguity.

We are now ready to take up the question, "Which state of the Union is farthest east and which is farthest west?" To me, it seems that the clearest way to do this is to pick some point within the United States from which we can travel east or west to the farthest limit of American territory without, in either case, traveling more than 180°.

If we consider only the forty-eight contiguous states, we can use as our reference meridian the one marked 100.0°W on our maps. That's a nice even number and the meridian cuts right through the middle of Nebraska besides and that's close enough to the middle of the country.

As one follows the meridian lines eastward, one reaches the Atlantic Ocean off the state of Georgia. Continue moving eastward, and state after state falls behind until only New England is left. And then, finally, only Maine is left.

The easternmost portion of Maine is at a city appropriately named Eastport, which lies 33.0° east of our reference meridian. Consequently, it seems fair to decide that of the forty-eight states, Maine is most easterly.

Now let's move westward. If it is your impression that California is the most westerly state of the forty-eight, forget it. The most westerly portion of California is Cape Mendocino on its northern coast and it lies about 24.1° west of the reference meridian. Oregon does a little better, for Cape Blanco on its southern shore is 24.5° west of the reference meridian.

It is the state of Washington that holds the record, however, for Cape Flattery at the northwestern tip of the Olympic Peninsula, touches a point 24.8° west of the reference meridian.

Of the forty-eight states, then, Maine is easternmost and Washington westernmost.

What, though, if you add the forty-ninth and fiftieth states, Alaska and Hawaii? A quick glance at the map shows you that both new states lie to the west of the forty-eight. Therefore, they leave Maine in undisputed possession of the eastern championship but must decide the western championship between themselves.

The main portion of Hawaii consists of eight islands of which the most westerly is Niihau, which reaches 60.2° west of the reference meridian.

However, Hawaii can do even better than this. West of the main island lie a string of small islands, shoals, and reefs (the Leeward Islands) which reach out for nearly 1,500 miles in a northwesterly direction. All of them are part of the state of Hawaii though they are virtually uninhabited, and serve mainly as the Hawaiian Islands Bird Reservation.

The westernmost of these is Kure Island (also called Ocean Island) which is somewhat smaller than Manhattan and which lies 78.5° west of the reference meridian.

And Alaska? Can that do better?

Alaska extends westward into four peninsulas, of which the second from the top, Seward Peninsula, reaches most westerly, and is the most westerly part, in fact, of the North American mainland. It ends in Cape Prince of Wales, which is 68.0° west of the reference meridian. This beats out the Hawaiian main islands, but not the Leeward Islands extension.

However, Alaska has an island chain of its own. Extending from the southernmost peninsula (Alaska Peninsula) are an arc of islands called the Aleutian Islands.

The Aleutians are unusual in that they extend Alaska farther to the south than most people would imagine. The southernmost Aleutian island is Amchitka, which is at a latitude of about 51.7°N (just about the latitude of London). This means that there are parts of Alaska which are farther south than Berlin or Warsaw.

But it is the westerly reach that now concerns us. The islands stretch across 1,200 miles of the Pacific and the most westerly of the group to form part of Alaska is the island of Attu. (It and the nearby island of Kiska were occupied for a while by the Japanese during World War II, the only part of the fifty states to suffer this indignity—though to be sure, Alaska was not then a state.) Attu is 87.4° west of the reference meridian, and Alaska, then, is the most westerly state.

25

To summarize, then— In answering the question concerning the extreme states of the Union, I made some quick judgments in my mind and came up with:

|  | MY ANSWER | BOOK ANSWER |
|---|---|---|
| south | Hawaii | Hawaii |
| north | Alaska | Alaska |
| west | Alaska | Alaska |
| east | Maine | Alaska |

(And how did you do?)

Why the discrepancy about the easternmost state? Well, I made use of a reference meridian that made it convenient to estimate east and west in the United States. To do the same for Europe I would have used a different reference meridian, for China still a different one, and so on. This sort of thing was also done, more or less officially, by the various seagoing nations, until it was finally decided to establish a single reference meridian for the use of everyone.

This overall reference is the Prime Meridian, which passes through Greenwich Observatory in London. Everything west of that is marked off in degrees West Longitude; everything east in East Longitude. The two types of longitude meet at 180.0°, which is the meridian directly antipodal to the Prime Meridian.

We might possibly, then, define any point in East Longitude as east of any point in West Longitude. Of two objects, both in East Longitude, the one with the higher degree value is more easterly; of two objects, both in West Longitude, the one with the lower degree value is more easterly.

By this convention, an object is farthest east, if it passes beyond 179.0°E to touch 180.0° and farthest west if it passes beyond 179.0°W to touch 180.0°. At 180.0°, east is west and west is east and always the twain shall meet.

Naturally, the 180.0° line can introduce east-west confusion, but by a fortunate coincidence, it passes over nearly the minimum of land and the maximum of water (making possible a very convenient International Date Line).

All the forty-eight states, fortunately, are in West Longitude. The easternmost point of Maine is at 67.0° W and the westernmost point of Washington is at 124.8°W. Even Hawaii does not extend quite to the confusion of the 180.0° line, for Kure Island is at 178.5°W, just 1.5° short of the fatal mark.

But Alaska?

Well, the 180.0° line passes right through the Aleutian Islands, leaving a stretch of about three hundred miles of the islands beyond that crucial line and, therefore, in East Longitude. Attu, for instance is at 172.6° E. The island nearest the 180.0° line from the East Longitude side is Semisopochnoi Island (the Aleutians were once Russian territory, you know), which reaches a longitude of about 179.85°E.

Semisopochnoi Island has the highest value of East Longitude of any land area forming part of the fifty states and, by the east-west convention of the Prime Meridian, is therefore the most easterly portion of the fifty states. From this standpoint, Alaska is the most easterly state, as well as the most westerly and northerly.

However, I consider that a highly artificial and strained viewpoint. Imagine you are standing on Tanaga Island, an Aleutian island at roughly 179.0°W, and are being asked where Semisopochnoi Island is. Are you going to point and say, "Oh about 100 miles west."? Or are you going to point in the opposite direction and say, "Oh, about 13,900 miles east."?

So I reject the east-west convention based on the Prime Meridian, which is based on the purely man-made accident of its placing, and upon the agreement to number from the Prime Meridian in both directions instead of in one direction only, sweeping all the way round to 360.0°.

Having rejected that, I insist on insisting that Maine is the most easterly of the fifty states.

–With all due respect to the Gentle Readers in the great state of Alaska, of course.

# 2. WATER, WATER, EVERYWHERE —

THE ONE TIME in my adult life that I indulged in an ocean voyage, it wasn't voluntary. Some nice sergeants were herding a variety of young men in soldier suits on to a vessel and I was one of the young men.

I didn't really want to leave land (being a lubber of the most fearful variety) and meant to tell the sergeants so. However, they seemed *so* careworn with their arduous duties, *so* melancholy at having to undertake the uncongenial task of telling other people what to do, that I didn't have the heart. I was afraid that if they found out one of the soldiers didn't really want to go, they might cry.

So I went aboard and we began the long six-day ocean voyage from San Francisco to Hawaii.

A luxury cruise it was not. The bunks were stacked four high and so were the soldiers. Seasickness was rampant and while I myself was not seasick even once (on my honor as a science fiction fan) that doesn't mean much when the guy in the bunk above decides to be.

My most grievous shock came the first night. I had been withstanding the swaying of the ship all day and had waited patiently for bedtime. Bedtime came; I got into my non-luxurious bunk and suddenly realized that *they didn't turn off the ocean at night!* The boat kept swaying, pitching, yawing, heaving, rolling, and otherwise making a jackass of itself all night long! And every night!

You may well imagine, then, that what with one thing and another, I made that cruise in grim-lipped silence and was notable above all other men on board ship for my surly disposition.

Except once. On the third day out, it rained. Nothing remarkable, you think? Remember, I'm a landlubber. I had never seen it rain on the ocean; I had never *thought* of rain on the ocean. And now I saw it—a complete waste of effort. Tons of water hurling down for nothing; just landing in more water.

The thought of the futility of it all; of the inefficiency and sheer ridiculousness of a planetary design that allowed rain upon the ocean struck me so forcibly that I burst into laughter. The laughter fed upon itself and in no time at all, I was down on the deck, howling madly and flailing my arms and legs in wild glee—and getting rained on.

A sergeant (or somebody) approached and said, with warm and kindly sympathy, "What the hell's the matter with you, soldier? On your feet!"

And all I could say was, "It's raining! It's raining on the ocean!"

I kept on tittering about it all day, and that night all the bunks in the immediate neighborhood of mine were empty. The word had gone about (I imagine) that I was mad, and might turn homicidal at any moment.

But many times since, I have realized I shouldn't have laughed. I should have cried.

We here in the northeastern states are suffering from a serious drought and when I think of all the rain on the ocean and how nicely we could use a little bit of that rain on particular portions of dry land, I could cry right now.

I'll console myself as best I may, then, by talking about water.

Actually, the Earth is not short of water and never will be. In fact, we are in serious and continuing danger of too much water, if the warming trend continues and the ice caps melt.

But let's not worry about melting ice caps right now; let's just consider the Earth's water supply. To begin with, there is the ocean. I use the singular form of the noun because there is actually only one World Ocean; a continuous sheet of salt water in which the continents are set as large islands.

The total surface area of the World Ocean is 139,480,-000 square miles, while the surface area of the entire planet is 196,950,000 square miles. As you see, then, the World Ocean covers seventy-one percent of the Earth's surface.

The World Ocean is arbitrarily divided into smaller units partly because, in the early age of exploration, men weren't sure that there was a single ocean (this was first clearly demonstrated by the circumnavigation of the Earth by Magellan's expedition in 1519–1522) and partly because the continents do break up the World Ocean into joined segments which it is convenient to label separately.

Traditionally, one hears of the "Seven Seas" and indeed my globe and my various atlases do break up the World Ocean into seven subdivisions: 1) North Pacific, 2) South Pacific, 3) North Atlantic, 4) South Atlantic, 5) Indian, 6) Arctic, 7) Antarctic.

In addition, there are the smaller seas and bays and gulfs; portions of the ocean which are nearly surrounded by land as in the case of the Mediterranean Sea or the Gulf of Mexico or marked off from the main body of the ocean by a line of islands, as in the case of the Caribbean Sea or the South China Sea.

Let's simplify this arrangement as far as possible. In the first place, let's consider all seas, bays, and gulfs to be part of the ocean they adjoin. We can count the Mediterranean Sea, the Gulf of Mexico, and the Carib-

31

bean Sea as part of the North Atlantic, while the South China Sea is part of the North Pacific.

Second, there is no geophysical point in separating the North Pacific from the South Pacific, or the North Atlantic from the South Atlantic. (The conventional arbitrary dividing line in each case is the equator). Let's deal with a single Pacific Ocean and a single Atlantic Ocean.

Third, if you will look at a globe, you will see that the Arctic Ocean is not a truly separate ocean. It is an offshoot of the Atlantic Ocean to which it is connected by a thousand-mile-wide passage (the Norwegian Sea) between Greenland and Norway. Let's add the Arctic to the Atlantic, therefore.

Fourth, there is no Antarctic Ocean. The name is given to the stretch of waters neighboring Antarctica (which is the only portion of the globe where one can circumnavigate the planet along a parallel of latitude without being obstructed by land or by solid ice sheets.) However, there are no nonarbitrary boundaries between this stretch of water and the larger oceans to the north. The length of arbitrary boundary can be shortened by dividing the Antarctic among those larger oceans.

That leaves us, then, with exactly three large divisions of the World Ocean—the Pacific Ocean, the Atlantic Ocean, and the Indian Ocean.

If you look at a globe, you will see that the Pacific Ocean and Atlantic Ocean stretch from north polar regions to south polar regions. The division between them in the north is clear-cut, since the only connection is through the narrow Bering Strait between Alaska and Siberia. A short arbitrary line, fifty-six miles in length can be drawn across that stretch of water to separate the oceans.

In the south the division is less clear cut. An arbitrary line must be drawn across Drake Passage from the southernmost point of South America to the northernmost point of the Antarctic Peninsula. This line is about six hundred miles long.

The Indian Ocean is the stubby one, stretching only from the tropics to the Antarctic Ocean (though it makes up for that by being wider than the Atlantic, which is the skinny one.) The Indian Ocean is less conveniently separated from the other oceans. A north-south line from the southernmost points of Africa and Australia to Antarctica will separate the Indian Ocean from the Atlantic and Pacific respectively. The first of these lines is about twenty-five hundred miles long and the second eighteen hundred miles long, which makes the demarcation pretty vague, but then I told you there's really only one ocean. In addition, the Indonesian islands separate the Pacific from the Indian.

The surface area of the three oceans, using these conventions, are expressed in Table 1 in round figures:

*Table 1—Area of the Oceans*

|  | SURFACE AREA (SQUARE MILES) | PERCENT OF WORLD OCEAN |
|---|---|---|
| Pacific | 68,000,000 | 48.7 |
| Atlantic | 41,500,000 | 29.8 |
| Indian | 30,000,000 | 21.5 |

As you see, the Pacific Ocean is as large as the Atlantic and Indian put together. The Pacific Ocean is, by itself, twenty percent larger than all of Earth's land area. It's a big glob of water.

I was aware of this when I crossed the Pacific (well, half of it anyway) and I was also aware that when I was looking at all that water, I was seeing only the top of it.

The Pacific Ocean is not only the most spread out of the oceans but the deepest, with an average depth of about 2.6 miles. In comparison, the Indian Ocean has an average depth of about 2.4 miles and the Atlantic only about 2.1 miles. We can therefore work out the volume of the different oceans, as in Table 2.

As you see then the water of the World Ocean is distributed among the three oceans in just about the ratio of 2:1:1.

The total, 339,000,000 cubic miles, is a considerable amount. It makes up 1/800 of the volume of the Earth —a most respectable fraction. If it were all accumulated into one place it would form a sphere about 864 miles

*Table 2—Volume of the Oceans*

|         | VOLUME (CUBIC MILES) | PERCENT OF WORLD OCEAN |
|---------|----------------------|------------------------|
| Pacific | 177,000,000 | 52.2 |
| Atlantic | 87,000,000 | 25.7 |
| Indian | 75,000,000 | 22.1 |
| Total | 339,000,000 | |

in diameter. This is larger than any asteroid in the solar system, probably larger than all the asteroids put together.

There is therefore no shortage of water. If the oceans were divided up among the population of the Earth, each man, woman, and child would get a tenth of a cubic mile of ocean water. If you think that's not much (just a miserable tenth of a single cubic mile), consider that that equals 110,000,000,000 gallons.

Of course, the ocean consists of sea water, which has limited uses. You can travel over it and swim in it—but you can't (without treatment) drink it, water your lawn with it, wash efficiently with it, or use it in industrial processes.

For all such vital operations, you need fresh water, and there the ready-made supply is much more limited. Ocean water (including a bit of inland salt water) makes up about 98.4 percent of all the water on Earth;

and fresh water makes up 1.6 percent or about 5,800,000 cubic miles.

That doesn't sound too bad, but it's not the whole story. Fresh water exists in three phases, solid, liquid, and gaseous. (And, incidentally, let me interrupt myself to say that water is the *only* common substance on Earth that exists in all three phases; and the only one to exist chiefly in the liquid phase. All other common substances either exist solely in the gaseous state, as do oxygen and nitrogen; or solely in the solid state, as do silica and hematite.) The distribution of the fresh water supply of the Earth among the three phases is as shown in Table 3:

*Table 3—The Fresh Water Supply*

|  | VOLUME (CUBIC MILES) |
|---|---|
| Ice | 5,680,000 |
| Liquid fresh water | 120,000 |
| Water vapor (if condensed to liquid) | 3,400 |

Most of Earth's supply of fresh water is unavailable to us because it is tied up as ice. It is, of course, quite possible and even simple to melt ice, but the problem is one of location. Nearly ninety percent of the world's ice is compacted into the huge ice cap that covers Antarctica and most of the rest into the smaller sheet that covers Greenland. What's left (about 200,000 cubic miles) occurs as glaciers in the higher mountains and the smaller Arctic islands plus some polar sea ice. All of this ice is quite out of the way.

That leaves us with just under 125,000 cubic miles of fresh water in liquid and gaseous form, and this represents the most valuable portion of the water resources of the planet. The fresh water supply is constantly running off into the sea through flowing rivers and seeping ground water, or evaporating into the air. This loss, however, is constantly replaced by rainfall. It is estimated that the total rainfall on all the land areas of the world amounts to 30,000 cubic miles per year. This means that one-quarter of the fresh water supply is replaced each year and if there were no rain at all anywhere, Earth's dry land would become dry indeed, for in four years (if one assumes that the rate of flow, seepage, and evaporation remains constant) fresh water would be all gone.

If Earth's fresh water were evenly distributed among humanity, every man, woman, and child would own 40,000,000 gallons and every year he could use 10,000,000 gallons of his supply, collecting rain replacement in return.

But alas, the fresh water is not evenly distributed. Some areas on Earth have a far greater supply than they can use and other areas are parched. The maldistribution works in time as well as in space; for an area which is flooded one year may be drought-stricken the next.

The most spectacular reservoirs of fresh water are the lakes of the world. Of course, not all enclosed bodies of water are fresh. Only those bodies of water are fresh which have outlets to the ocean so that the efflux of water removes the salt dissolved out of the land and brought into the lake. Where a lake has no outlet to the ocean, it can lose water only through evaporation and the dissolved salts do not evaporate. More salt is constantly brought in by rivers feeding into the enclosed body and the result is a salt lake which, in some cases, is far saltier than the sea.

In fact, the largest inland body of water in the world —the Caspian Sea, located between the Soviet Union and Iran—is not fresh water. It has an area of 169,381 square miles, just about the size of California and it has 3,370 miles of shoreline.

It is sometimes stated that the Caspian Sea is not a sea but merely a lake, although a very large one. However, it seems to me that "lake" might well be restricted to enclosed bodies of *fresh* water. If "sea" is taken to mean salt water, whether in the ocean or not, then the Caspian is indeed the Caspian *Sea*.

The Caspian Sea is only 0.6 percent salt (as compared to the 3.5 percent salt of the oceans) but this is enough to make the waters of the Caspian undrinkable, except in the northwest corner where the fresh waters of the Volga River are discharged.

About 150 miles east of the Caspian is the Aral Sea, which is about 1.1 percent salt. It is twice as salty as the Caspian Sea, but it is much smaller in extent, with a surface area of only about 26,000 square miles—though that is enough to make it the fourth-largest body of enclosed water in the world.

There are two other notable enclosed bodies of salt water. One is the Great Salt Lake (which I would much prefer to call the Utah Sea, since it is not "great," nor, by my definition, a lake) and the other is the Dead Sea. The Great Salt Lake is only 1,500 square miles in area and the Dead Sea is smaller still—370 square miles. The Dead Sea is not much larger, in fact, than the five boroughs of New York City.

Nevertheless, these two relatively small bodies of water, are unusual for extreme salinity. The Great Salt Lake is about fifteen percent salt and the Dead Sea is about twenty-five percent salt, four times and seven times (respectively) as salty as the ocean.

However, looking at the surface of the water can be deceptive. How deep are these four inland seas? From data on the depth, we can work out the volume of each and the total salt* content, as in Table 4:

*The salt is not entirely sodium chloride by any means, but that's another matter.

### Table 4—The Inland Seas

|  | AVERAGE DEPTH (FEET) | VOLUME (CUBIC MILES) | TOTAL SALT (TONS) |
|---|---|---|---|
| Caspian Sea | 675 | 21,600 | 600,000,000,000 |
| Aral Sea | 53 | 260 | 13,000,000,000 |
| Dead Sea | 1,080 | 75 | 86,500,000,000 |
| Great Salt Lake | 20 | 5.7 | 4,000,000,000 |

As you see, the tiny Dead Sea isn't so tiny after all. In terms of quantity of water it is much larger than the Great Salt Lake, and it contains 6½ times as much salt as the apparently much larger Aral Sea.

But let's turn to the true lakes—the enclosed bodies of fresh water. The largest such body in terms of surface area is Lake Superior, which is about as large as the state of South Carolina. It is usually listed as the second-largest enclosed body of water on Earth (though, as I will show, it isn't really). It is to be sure, a very poor second to the mighty Caspian, covering less than one-fifth the area of that body of water but remember, the water of Lake Superior is fresh.)

Lake Superior is, however, only one of five American Great Lakes that are usually treated as separate bodies of water but which are neighboring and interconnected so that it is really quite fair to consider them all as making up one huge basin of fresh water. Statistics concerning them follow in Table 5:

### Table 5—The American Great Lakes

|  | AREA (SQUARE MILES) | RANK IN SIZE | AVERAGE DEPTH (FEET) | VOLUME (CUBIC MILES) |
|---|---|---|---|---|
| Superior | 31,820 | 2 | 900 | 5,400 |
| Huron | 23,010 | 5 | 480 | 2,100 |
| Michigan | 22,400 | 6 | 600 | 2,600 |

| Erie | 9,940 | 12 | 125 | 240 |
|------|-------|-----|-----|-----|
| Ontario | 7,540 | 14 | 540 | 770 |
| Total | 94,710 | | | 11,110 |

Taken as a unit, as they should be, the American Great Lakes have a little over half the surface area and volume of the Caspian Sea. And they contain nearly one-tenth the total fresh water supply of the planet.

The only other group of lakes that can even faintly compare with the American Great Lakes are a similar series, considerably more separated, in East Africa. The largest are Lakes Victoria, Tanganyika, and Nyasa, which I can lump together as the African Great Lakes. Here are the statistics in Table 6:

### Table 6—The African Great Lakes

| | AREA (SQUARE MILES) | RANK IN SIZE | AVERAGE DEPTH (FEET) | VOLUME (CUBIC MILES) |
|------|------|------|------|------|
| Victoria | 26,200 | 3 | 240 | 1,200 |
| Tanganyika | 12,700 | 8 | 1,900 | 4,500 |
| Nyasa | 11,000 | 10 | 1,800 | 3,800 |
| | 49,900 | | | 9,500 |

The African Great Lakes (two of them at least) are remarkable for their depth, so that although they occupy an area of only slightly more than half that of the American Great Lakes, the volume of fresh water they contain almost rivals that present in our own larger but shallower lakes.

But if we're going to talk about deep lakes, we've got to mention Lake Baikal in south-central Siberia. Its area is 13,197 square miles, making it the seventh-largest body of enclosed water on Earth, by the usual criterion of surface area. Its average depth however, is 2,300 feet, making it the deepest lake in the world. (Its maximum depth is 4,982 feet or nearly a mile. It is so deep, I was once told, that it is the only lake which contains the equivalent of deep-sea fish. If so, these are the only fresh-water, deep-sea fish in the world.)

Its depth means that Baikal contains 5,750 cubic miles of fresh water, more than that in Lake Superior.

The only remaining lakes that would fall in the category of "great lakes" are three in western Canada. The statistics on the average depth of these Canadian Great Lakes are virtually nonexistent. I have the figures on maximum depth for two of them and nothing at all for the third. However, I shall make what I hope is an intelligent guess just to see what things look like, and you will find that in Table 7:

*Table 7—The Canadian Great Lakes*

|  | AREA (SQUARE MILES) | RANK IN SIZE | AVERAGE DEPTH (FEET) | VOLUME (CUBIC MILES) |
|---|---|---|---|---|
| Great Bear | 12,200 | 9 | 240 | 525 |
| Great Slave | 10,719 | 11 | 240 | 510 |
| Winnipeg | 9,460 | 13 | 50 | 90 |

Now we are in a position to list the bodies of enclosed water in the order of their real size, their fluid contents rather than their surface area. To be sure, surface area of any lake can be determined with reasonable accuracy, whereas the fluid contents can only be roughly estimated, so it makes sense to list them in order of decreasing surface area. However, I will do as I choose. The fourteen largest bodies of enclosed water (in terms of surface area) rank in terms of fluid content as shown in Table 8.

This list is not only a very rough one, with several of the figures so rough as to be worthless but in addition there are lakes with smaller areas than any on the list which are deep enough to deserve a listing somewhere ahead of Winnipeg. These include Lake Ladoga and Lake Onega in the northwestern stretch of European Russia, and Lake Titicaca in the Andes between Bolivia and Peru.

*Table 8—The Large Lakes of the Earth*

|  | VOLUME (CUBIC MILES) |
|---|---|
| *Caspian | 21,600 |
| Baikal | 5,750 |
| Superior | 5,400 |
| Tanganyika | 4,500 |
| Nyasa | 3,800 |
| Michigan | 2,600 |
| Huron | 2,100 |
| Victoria | 1,200 |
| Ontario | 770 |
| Great Bear | 525 |
| Great Slave | 510 |
| *Aral | 260 |
| Erie | 240 |
| Winnipeg | 90 |

*do not contain fresh water

But what's the use? All this talk about water isn't helping the parching Northeast at all. Indeed, the water level in the American Great Lakes has been falling disturbingly in recent years, I understand, and even the Caspian Sea is shrinking.

Maybe old Mother Earth is getting tired of us. . . . In my more morose moments, I wonder if I could bring myself to blame her if she were.

# 3. UP AND DOWN THE EARTH

BOSTON IS GETTING its face lifted, and we now have "The New Boston."

The outstanding feature of the New Boston is the Prudential Center, which is an area of the Back Bay that has been renovated into New York-like luxury. It possesses a new hotel, the Sheraton-Boston, and, most spectacular of all, a beautiful skyscraper, the fifty-two-story Prudential Tower, which is 750 feet tall.

In the summer of 1965, I invaded the center for the first time. I was asked to join a panel discussion dealing with the future of industrial management. The panel was held in the Sheraton-Boston under conditions of great splendor, and after the dinner that followed, the manager of the hotel announced, in the course of a short talk, that the Prudential Tower was the tallest office building in continental North America.

We registered amazement and he at once explained that yes, there were indeed taller office buildings not far from Boston, but they were not on continental North America. They were on an island off the shores of the continent; an island named Manhattan.

And he was right. Outside the island of Manhattan, there is, at the moment of writing, no office building taller than the Prudential Tower anywhere in North America. (Perhaps anywhere in the world.)

It made me think at once that you can play a large

number of games, if you are the record-gathering type (as I am), by altering qualifications slightly. Long before the manager's speech was over, I was thinking of mountains.

Everyone knows the name of the highest mountain of the world. It is Mount Everest, located in the Himalayan Mountain Range, exactly on the border between Nepal and Tibet.

It is named for a British military engineer, George Everest, who spent much of his adult life surveying Java and India and who, from 1830 to 1843, was surveyor general of India. In 1852, when a mountain was discovered in the north, one which was at once suspected of being height champion, it was named for him. At that, his name is easier to pronounce than the native Tibetan name for the mountain—Chomolungma.

The height of Mount Everest is usually given in the reference books as 29,002 feet above sea level, a value first obtained in 1860, though I believe that the most recent trigonometric measurements make it 29,141 feet. In either case, the tippy, tippy top of Mount Everest is the only piece of solid land on the face of the globe that is more than 29,000 feet above sea level, so that the mountain qualifies nicely as something quite unique. Using another unit of measure, Mount Everest is just a trifle more than five and a half miles high and all other land is less than five and a half miles above sea level.

Except by members of the "Anglo-Saxon nations," however, mountain heights are generally measured in meters rather than in feet or miles. There are 3.28 feet in a meter and Mount Everest stands 8,886 meters above sea level.

At once this gives rise to the question: how many other mountains are there that belong to the rarefied aristocracy of those that tower more than 8,000 meters above sea level. The answer is: Not many. Just thirteen!

And here they are in Table 9.

### Table 9—The 8,000-Meter Mountains

| | | HEIGHT | |
|---|---|---|---|
| MOUNTAINS | FEET | MILES | METERS |
| Everest | 29,141 | 5.52 | 8,886 |
| Godwin Austen | 28,250 | 5.36 | 8,613 |
| Kanchenjunga | 28,108 | 5.33 | 8,570 |
| Lhotse | 27,923 | 5.29 | 8,542 |
| Makalu | 27,824 | 5.28 | 8,510 |
| Dhaulagiri | 26,810 | 5.10 | 8,175 |
| Manaslu | 26,760 | 5.06 | 8,159 |
| Cho Oyu | 26,750 | 5.06 | 8,155 |
| Nanga Parbat | 26,660 | 5.05 | 8,125 |
| Annapurna | 26,504 | 5.03 | 8,080 |
| Gasherbrum | 26,470 | 5.02 | 8,075 |
| Broad | 26,400 | 5.00 | 8,052 |
| Gosainthan | 26,291 | 4.98 | 8,016 |

Of these thirteen aristocrats all but four are in the Himalaya Mountain Range, spread out over a stretch of a little over three hundred miles. The tallest exception is Mount Godwin Austen, which is named for Henry Haversham Godwin-Austen, another Britisher who was engaged in the nineteenth-century trigonometric surveys of India. It is only recently that the mountain came to be officially known by his name. Previously, it was known simply as K-2. Its native name is Dapsang.

Mount Godwin Austen is located about eight hundred miles northwest of Mount Everest and the other Himalayan towers. It is the highest peak of the Karakorum Mountain Range, running between Kashmir and Sinkiang.

All thirteen of the eight-thousanders are located in Asia and all are located in the borderlands that separate India and China.

This is true, indeed, not only for the thirteen highest but for the sixty highest (!) mountains in the world, at least, so that the area is *the* place for mountaineers.

And of all mountains, Everest is obviously *the* mountain to climb. The first serious attempt to climb it was made in 1922 and after a full generation of effort, eleven lives were lost on its slopes and no successes were scored. Then, on May 29, 1953, the New Zealander Edmund Percival Hillary and the Sherpa Tenzing Norkey made it. Since then, others have too.

You would think that with even Everest conquered, there would remain no more mountains unclimbed, but that is not so. Everest received a lot more attention than some of the other peaks. As of now (unless someone has sneaked up the slopes while I wasn't looking) the highest mountain still unconquered is Gosainthan, which is only the thirteenth highest.

The highest mountain range outside Asia is the Andes Mountain Range, running down the western edge of South America. The highest peak in the Andes is Mount Aconcagua, which stands 22,834 feet high. Despite the fact that Mount Aconcagua is the highest mountain peak in the world outside Asia, there are scores of higher peaks in Asia.

For the records, here, in Table 10, are the highest peaks in each of the continents. To soothe my national and regional pride, I will add the highest mountain in the forty-eight contiguous states, and in New England, too. (After all, I'm writing the chapter and can do as I please.)

To locate these mountains—

Mount Aconcagua is in Argentina, very close to the border of Chile, only a hundred miles east of Valparaiso.

Mount McKinley is in south-central Alaska, about one hundred fifty miles southwest of Fairbanks. The fact that it was the highest land in North America was discovered in 1896 and it was named after William McKinley, who had just been elected President of the United States. The Russians (who had owned Alaska before 1867) had called it "Bolshaya" ("large").

Mount Kilimanjaro is in northeastern Tanganyika, near the border of Kenya, and is about two hundred

*Table 10—The Highest Mountains by Regions*

| | | HEIGHT | | |
|---|---|---|---|---|
| REGION | MOUNTAIN | FEET | MILES | METERS |
| Asia | Everest | 29,141 | 5.52 | 8,886 |
| South America | Aconcagua | 22,834 | 4.34 | 6,962 |
| North America | McKinley | 20,320 | 3.85 | 6,195 |
| Africa | Kilimanjaro | 19,319 | 3.67 | 5,890 |
| Europe | Elbrus | 18,481 | 3.50 | 5,634 |
| Antarctica | Vinson Massif | 16,860 | 3.19 | 5,080 |
| 48 States | Whitney | 14,496 | 2.75 | 4,419 |
| Australia | Kosciusko | 7,328 | 1.39 | 2,204 |
| New England | Washington | 6,288 | 1.19 | 1,918 |

miles from the Indian Ocean. Mount Elbrus is in the Caucasus Mountain Range, about sixty miles northeast of the Black Sea.

Concerning the Vinson Massif, alas, I know virtually nothing. Even its height is only a rough estimate.

Mount Whitney is in California, on the eastern border of Sequoia National Park. It is only eighty miles west of Death Valley in which is to be found the lowest point of land in the forty-eight states (a pool called Badwater —and I'll bet it is—which is two hundred eighty feet below sea level). Mount Whitney is named for the American geologist Josiah Dwight Whitney, who measured its height in 1864.

Mount Kosciusko is in the southeastern corner of Australia, on the boundary between the states of Victoria and New South Wales. It is the highest point of the range called the Australian Alps. I suspect it was discovered at the end of the eighteenth century, when the Polish patriot Thaddeus Kosciusko was leading the last, forlorn fight for Polish independence, but I can't be sure.

Mount Washington is located in the Presidential Mountain Range in northern New Hampshire, and we all know who it is named after.

46

By listing the high mountains by continents, I don't mean to imply that all high mountains are on continents. In fact, Australia, usually considered a continent (though a small one) possesses no particularly high mountains, while New Guinea to its north (definitely an island, though a large one) is much more mountainous and possesses dozens of peaks higher than any in continental Australia, and some that are quite respectable by any standards. Three Pacific islands are notably mountainous and these are listed in Table 11.

*Table 11—Notable Island Mountains*

| | | HEIGHT | | |
| ISLAND | MOUNTAIN | FEET | MILES | METERS |
| --- | --- | --- | --- | --- |
| New Guinea | Carstensz | 16,404 | 3.12 | 5,000 |
| Hawaii | { Mauna Kea | 13,784 | 2.61 | 4,200 |
| | Mauna Loa | 13,680 | 2.59 | 4,171 |
| Sumatra | Kerintji | 12,484 | 2.36 | 3,807 |
| New Zealand | Cook | 12,349 | 2.34 | 3,662 |

Mount Carstensz is the highest mountain in the world that is not on a continent. Who it is named for I do not know, but it is in the western portion of New Guinea and is part of the Nassau Mountain Range, which is named for the Dutch royal family. I suspect that by now Indonesia has renamed both the range and the mountain or, more likely, has restored the original names, but I don't know what these might be.

Mount Cook is just a little west of center in New Zealand's southern island. It is named for the famous explorer Captain Cook, of course, and its Maori name is Aorangi.

All the heights I have given for the mountains, so far, are "above sea level."

However, remembering the manager of the Sheraton-Boston Hotel, let's improve the fun by qualifying matters.

After all, the height of a mountain depends a good

deal upon the height of its base. The Himalayan mountain peaks are by far the most majestic in the world; there is no disputing that. Nevertheless, it is also true that they sit upon the Tibetan plateau, which is the highest in the world. The Tibetan "lowlands" are nowhere lower than some 12,000 feet above sea level.

If we subtract 12,000 feet from Mount Everest's height, we can say that its peak is only 17,000 feet above the land mass upon which it rests.

This is not exactly contemptible, but by this new standard (base to top, instead of sea level to top) are there any mountains that are higher than Mount Everest? Yes, indeed, there are, and the new champion is not in the Himalayas, or in Asia, or on any continent.

This stands to reason after all. Suppose you had a mountain on a relatively small island. That island may *be* the mountain, and the mountain wouldn't look impressive because it was standing with its base in the ocean depth and with the ocean lapping who knows how many feet up its slopes.

This is actually the case for a particular island. That island is Hawaii—the largest single unit of the Hawaiian Islands. The island of Hawaii, with an area of 4,021 square miles (about twice the size of Delaware) is actually a huge mountain rising out of the Pacific. It comes to four peaks, of which the two highest are Mauna Kea and Mauna Loa (*see* Table 11).

The mountain that makes up Hawaii is a volcano actually, but most of it is extinct. Mauna Loa alone remains active. It, all by itself, is the largest single mountain in the world in terms of cubic content of rock, so you can imagine how large the whole mountain above and below sea level must be.

The central crater pit of Mauna Loa is sometimes active but has not actually erupted in historical times. Instead, the lava flow comes from openings on the sides. The largest of these is Kilauea, which is on the eastern side of Mauna Loa, some 4,088 feet (0.77 miles, or

1,246 meters) above sea level. Kilauea is the largest active crater in the world and is more than two miles in diameter.

As though these distinctions are not enough, this tremendous four-peaked mount we call Hawaii becomes totally astounding if viewed as a whole. If one plumbs the ocean depths, one finds that Hawaii stands on a land base that is over 18,000 feet below sea level.

If the oceans were removed from Earth's surface (only temporarily, please), then no single mountain on Earth could possibly compare with the breathtaking towering majesty of Hawaii. It would be by far the tallest mountain on Earth, counting from base to peak. Its height on that basis would be 32,036 feet (6.08 miles or 9,767 meters.) It is the only mountain on earth that extends more than six miles from base to tip.

The vanishing of the ocean would reveal a similar, though smaller, peak in the Atlantic Ocean; one that is part of the Mid-Atlantic Mountain Range. For the most part, we are unaware of this mountain range because it is drowned by the ocean, but it is larger and longer and more spectacular than any of the mountain ranges on dry land, even than the Himalayas. It is 7,000 miles long and 500 miles wide and that's not bad.

Some of the highest peaks of the range do manage to poke their heads above the surface of the Atlantic. The Azores, a group of nine islands and several islets (belonging to Portugal), are formed in this manner. They are about 800 miles west of Portugal and have a total land area of 888 square miles, rather less than that of Rhode Island.

On Pico Island in the Azores stands the highest point of land on the island group. This is Pico Alto ("High Mountain"), which reaches 7,460 feet (1.42 miles or 2,274 meters) above sea level. However, if you slide down the slopes of the mountain and proceed all the way down to the sea bottom, you find that only one-quarter of the mountain shows above water.

49

The total height of Pico Alto from underwater base to peak is about 27,500 feet (5.22 miles or 8,384 meters), which makes it a peak of Himalayan dimensions.

While we have the oceans temporarily gone from the Earth, we might as well see how deep the ocean goes.

About 1.2 percent of the sea bottom lies more than 6,000 meters below sea level, and where this happens we have the various "Trenches." There are a number of these, most of them in the Pacific Ocean. All are near island chains and presumably the same process that burrows out the deeps also heaves up the island chain.

The greatest depth so far recorded in some of these deeps (according to the material available to me) is given in Table 12.

*Table 12—Some Ocean Trenches*

| TRENCH | GENERAL LOCATION | DEPTH FEET | MILES | METERS |
|--------|------------------|------|-------|--------|
| Bartlett | S. of Cuba | 22,788 | 4.31 | 6,948 |
| Java | S. of Java | 24,442 | 4.64 | 7,252 |
| Puerto Rico | N. of Puerto Rico | 30,184 | 5.71 | 9,392 |
| Japan | S. of Japan | 32,153 | 6.09 | 9,800 |
| Kurile | E. of Kamchatka | 34,580 | 6.56 | 10,543 |
| Tonga | E. of New Zealand | 35,597 | 6.75 | 10,853 |
| Mariana | E. of Guam | 35,800 | 6.79 | 10,915 |
| Mindanao | E. of Philippines | 36,198 | 6.86 | 11,036 |

The figures for the depth of the deeps are by no means as reliable as those for the heights of mountains, of course, and I can't tell when some oceanographic ship will plumb a deeper depth in one or more of these deeps. The greatest recorded depth in the Mindanao Trench—and in the world—was plumbed only as recently as March, 1959, by the Russian oceanographic vessel the *Vityaz*.

The greatest depth in the Mariana Trench was actually reached by Jacques Piccard and Don Walsh in person on January 23, 1960, in the bathyscaphe *Trieste*. This has been named the "Challenger Deep" in honor of the oceanographic vessel the H.M.S. *Challenger*, which conducted a scientific cruise from 1872 to 1876 all over the oceans and established modern oceanography.

In any case, the oceans are deeper than any mountain is high, which is the point I want to make, and in several places.

Consider the greatest depth of the Mindanao Trench. If Mount Everest could be placed in it and made to nestle all the way in, the mountain would sink below the waves and waters would roll for 7,000 feet (1⅓ miles) over its peak. If the island of Hawaii were moved from its present location, 4,500 miles westward, and sunk into the Mindanao Trench, it too would disappear entirely and 4,162 feet of water (⅘ of a mile) would flow above its tip.

If sea level is the standard, then the lowest bit of the solid land surface on Earth, just off the Philippines, is about 3,200 miles east of the highest bit at the top of Mount Everest. The total difference in height is 65,339 feet (12.3 miles or 19,921 meters.)

This sounds like a lot but the diameter of the Earth is about 7,900 miles so that this difference in low-high makes up only 0.15 percent of the Earth's total thickness.

If the Earth were shrunk to the size of my library globe (16 inches in diameter), the peak of Mount Everest would project only 0.011 inches above the surface and the Mindanao Trench would sink only 0.014 inches below the surface.

You can see then that despite all the extreme ups and downs I have been talking about, the surface of the Earth, viewed in proportion to the size of the Earth, is very smooth. It would be smooth, even if the oceans were gone and the unevennesses of the ocean bottom were exposed. With the oceans filling up most of the

Earth's hollows (and concealing the worst of the unevennesses), what remains is nothing.

But let's think about sea level again. If the Earth consisted of a universal ocean, it would take on the shape of an ellipsoid of revolution, thanks to the fact that the planet is rotating. It wouldn't be a perfect ellipsoid because, for various reasons, there are deviations of a few feet here and there. Such deviations are, however, of only the most academic interest and for our purposes we can be satisfied with the ellipsoid.

This means that if Earth were bisected by a plane cutting through the center, and through both poles, the cross-sectional outline would be an ellipse. The minor axis (or shortest possible Earth-radius) would be from the center to either pole, and that would be 6,356,912 meters. The longest radius, or major axis, is from the center to any point on the equator. This is 6,378,388 meters (on the average, if we wish to allow for the fact that the equator is itself very slightly elliptical.)

The equatorial sea level surface, then, is 21,476 meters (70,000 feet or 13.3 miles) further from the center than the polar sea level surface is. This is the well-known "equatorial bulge."

However, the bulge does not exist at the equator alone. The distance from center to sea level surface increases smoothly as one goes from the poles to the equator. Unfortunately, I have never seen any data on the extra length of the radius (over and above its minimum length at the poles) for different latitudes.

I have therefore had to calculate it for myself, making use of the manner in which the gravitational field varies from latitude to latitude. (I *could* find figures on the gravitational field.) The results, which I hope are approximately right anyway, are included in Table 13.

*Table 13—The Earth's Bulge*

|  | EXTRA LENGTH OF EARTH'S RADIUS | | |
| LATITUDE | FEET | MILES | METERS |
| 0° (equator) | 70,000 | 13.3 | 21,400 |
| 5° | 69,500 | 13.2 | 21,200 |
| 10° | 68,000 | 12.9 | 20,800 |
| 15° | 65,500 | 12.4 | 20,000 |
| 20° | 62,300 | 11.8 | 19,000 |
| 25° | 58,000 | 11.0 | 17,700 |
| 30° | 52,800 | 10.0 | 16,100 |
| 35° | 47,500 | 9.0 | 14,500 |
| 40° | 41,100 | 7.8 | 12,550 |
| 45° | 35,100 | 6.65 | 10,700 |
| 50° | 29,000 | 5.50 | 8,850 |
| 55° | 23,200 | 4.40 | 7,050 |
| 60° | 17,700 | 3.35 | 5,400 |
| 65° | 12,500 | 2.37 | 3,800 |
| 70° | 8,250 | 1.56 | 2,500 |
| 75° | 4,800 | 0.91 | 1,460 |
| 80° | 2,160 | 0.41 | 660 |
| 85° | 530 | 0.10 | 160 |
| 90° (poles) | 0 | 0.00 | 0 |

Suppose, now, we measure heights of mountains not from just any old sea level, but from the polar sea level. This would serve to compare distances *from the center of the Earth*, and certainly that is another legitimate way of comparing mountain heights.

If we did this, we would instantly get a completely new perspective on matters.

For instance, the Mindanao Trench dips down to 11,036 meters below sea level; but that means below the sea level at its own latitude, which is 10.0°N. That sea level is 20,800 meters above the polar sea level so that the greatest depth of the Mindanao Trench is still some 9,800 meters (6.1 miles) *above* the polar sea level.

In other words, when Peary stood on the sea ice at the North Pole, he was six miles closer to the center of the Earth than if he had been in a bathyscaphe probing the bottom of the Mindanao Trench.

Of course, the Arctic Ocean has a depth of its own. Depths of 4,500 meters (2.8 miles) have, I believe, been recorded in the Arctic. This means that the bottom of the Arctic Ocean is nearly nine miles closer to the center of the Earth than the bottom of the Mindanao Trench, and from this point of view, we have a new candidate for the mark of "deepest deep." (The south polar regions are filled up by the continent of Antarctica, so it is out of the running in this respect.)

And the mountains?

Mount Everest is at a latitude of about 30.0°. Sea level there is 16,100 meters higher than polar sea level. Add that to the 8,886 meters that Mount Everest is above its own sea level mark and you find that the mountain is just about 25,000 meters (15.5 miles) above polar sea level. But it is only 2.2 miles above equatorial sea level.

In other words, when a ship is crossing the equator, its passengers are only 2.2 miles closer to the center of the Earth than Hillary was when he stood on Mount Everest's peak.

Are there mountains that can do better than Mount Everest by this new standard? The other towers of Asia are in approximately Mount Everest's latitude. So are Mount Aconcagua and some of the other high peaks of the Andes (though on the other side of the equator).

Mount McKinley is a little over 60.0°N so that its sea level is only some 5,000 meters above polar sea level. Its total height above polar sea level is only 11,200 meters (7.0 miles), which is less than half the height of Mount Everest.

No, what we need are some good high mountains near the equator, where they can take full advantage of the maximum bulge of the Earth's midriff. A good candidate is the tallest mountain of Africa, Mount Kilimanjaro. It is about 3.0°S and is 5,890 meters high. To this one can add the 21,300-meter-high bulge it stands on, so that it is some 27,200 meters above polar sea level (16.9 miles), or nearly a mile and a half higher than Mount Everest, counting from the center of the Earth.

And that is not the best, either. My candidate for highest peak by these standards is Mount Chimborazo in Ecuador. It is part of the Andes Mountain Range, in which there are at least thirty peaks higher than Mount Chimborazo. Mount Chimborazo, is however, at 2.0°S. Its height above its own sea level is 6,300 meters. If we add the equatorial bulge, we have a total height of 27,600 meters above polar sea level (17.2 miles).

If we go by the distance from the center of the Earth, then, we can pass from the bottom of the Arctic Ocean to the top of Mount Chimborazo and increase that distance by 32,100 meters, or just about 20.0 miles —a nice even number.

By changing the point of view then, we have three different candidates for tallest mountain on Earth: Mount Everest, Mauna Kea, and Mount Chimborazo. We also have two different candidates for the deepest deep: the bottom of the Arctic Ocean and the bottom of the Mindanao Trench.

But let's face it. What counts in penetrating extreme depths or extreme heights is not mere distance, but difficulty of attainment. The greatest single measure of difficulty in plumbing depths is the increase of water pressure; and the greatest single measure of difficulty in climbing heights is the decrease of air pressure.

By that token, water pressure is highest at the bottom of the Mindanao Trench, and air pressure is lowest at the top of Mount Everest, and therefore those are the extremes in practice.

Just as (if the beans and cods will forgive me) the Empire State Building is the tallest office building in North America in practice, even though it is not, strictly speaking, actually on the North American continent.

# 4. THE ISLES OF EARTH

ONE OF THE NICEST THINGS about the science essays I write is the mail it brings me—almost invariably good-humored and interesting.

Consider, for instance, the previous chapter "Up and Down the Earth," in which I maintain that Boston's Prudential is the tallest office building on continental North America (as opposed to the higher ones on the *island* of Manhattan). The moment that essay first appeared I received a card from a resident of Greater Boston, advising me to follow the Charles and Neponset Rivers back to their source and see if Boston could not be considered an island.

I followed his advice and, in a way, he was right. The Charles River flows north of Boston and the Neponset River flows south of it. In southwestern Boston they approach within two and one-half miles of each other. Across that gap there meanders a stream from one to the other so that most of Boston and parts of some western suburbs (including the one I live in) are surrounded on all sides by surface water. The Prudential Tower, and my house, too, might therefore be considered, by a purist, to be located on an island.

*Well!*

But before I grow panicky, let me stop and consider. What is an island, anyway?

The word "island" comes from the Anglo-Saxon "eglond," and this may mean, literally, "water-land"; that is "land surrounded by water."

56

This Anglo-Saxon word, undergoing natural changes with time, ought to have come down to us as "eyland" or "iland." An "s" was mistakenly inserted, however, through the influence of the word "isle," which is synonymous with "island" yet, oddly enough, is not etymologically related to it.

For "isle" we have to go back to classical times.

The ancient Greeks in their period of greatness were a seafaring people who inhabited many islands in the Mediterranean Sea as well as sections of the mainland. They, and the Romans who followed, were well aware of the apparently fundamental difference between the two types of land. An island was to them a relatively small bit of land surrounded by the sea. The mainland (of which Greece and Italy were part) was, on the other hand, continuous land with no known boundary.

To be sure, the Greek geographers assumed that the land surface was finite and that the mainland was surrounded on all sides by a rim of ocean but, except for the west, that was pure theory. In the west, beyond the Strait of Gibraltar, the Mediterranean Sea did indeed open up into the broad ocean. No Greek or Roman, however, succeeded in traveling overland to Lapland, South Africa, or China, as to stand on the edge of land and, with his own eyes, gaze at the sea.

In Latin, then, the mainland was *terra continens;* that is, "land that holds together." The notion was that when you traveled on the mainland, there was always another piece of land holding on to the part you were traversing. There was no end. The phrase has come down to us as the word "continent."

On the other hand, a small bit of land, which did *not* hold together with the mainland, but which was separate and surrounded by the sea was *terra in salo* or "land in the sea." This shortened to *insula* in Latin; and, by successive steps, to *isola* in Italian, "isle" in English, and *île* in French.

The *strict* meaning of the word "isle," then, (and by

57

extension the word "island") is that of land surrounded by salt water. Of course, this is undoubtedly *too* strict. It would render Manhattan's status rather dubious since it is bounded on the west by the Hudson River. Then, too, there are certainly bodies of land, usually called islands, nestled within lakes or rivers, which are certainly surrounded by fresh water. However, even such islands must be surrounded by a thickness of water that is fairly large compared to the island's diameter. No one would dream of calling a large tract of land an island just because a creek marked it off. So Boston is *not* an island, practically speaking, and Manhattan is.

However, for the purposes of the remainder of this article I am going to stick to the strict definition of the term and discuss only those islands that are surrounded by salt water—

If we do this, however, then, again strictly speaking, the land surface of the Earth consists of nothing but islands. There are no continents in the literal meaning of the word. The mainland is never endless. The Venetian traveler Marco Polo reached the eastern edge of the anciently known mainland in 1275; the Portuguese navigator Bartholomew Diaz reached the southern edge in 1488; and Russian explorers marked off the northern edge in the seventeenth and early eighteenth centuries.

The mainland I refer to here is usually considered as making up the three continents of Asia, Europe, and Africa. But why *three* continents, where there is only a single continuous sheet of land, if one ignores rivers and the man-made Suez Canal?

The multiplicity of continents dates back to Greek days. The Greeks of Homeric times were concentrated on the mainland of Greece and faced a hostile second mainland to the east of the Aegean. The earliest Greeks had no reason to suspect that there was any land connection between the two mainlands and they gave them two different names; their own was Europe, the other Asia.

These terms are of uncertain origin but the theory I like best suggests they stem from the Semitic words *assu* and *erev*, meaning "east" and "west" respectively. (The Greeks may have picked up these words from the Phoenicians, by way of Crete, just as they picked up the Phoenician alphabet.) The Trojan War of 1200 B.C. begins the confrontation of, literally, the West and the East; a confrontation that is still with us.

Of course, Greek explorers must have learned, early in the game, that there was indeed a land connection between the two mainlands. The myth of Jason and the Argonauts, and their pursuit of the Golden Fleece, probably reflects trading expeditions antedating the Trojan War. The Argonauts reached Colchis (usually placed at the eastern extremity of the Black Sea) and there the two mainlands merged.

Indeed, as we now know, there is some fifteen hundred miles of land north of the Black Sea, and a traveler can pass from one side of the Aegean Sea to the other— from Europe to Asia and back—by way of this fifteen-hundred-mile connection. Consequently, Europe and Asia are separate continents only by geographic convention and there is no real boundary between them at all. The combined land mass is frequently spoken of as "Eurasia."

The Ural Mountains are arbitrarily set as the boundary between Europe and Asia in the geography books. Partly, this is because the Urals represent a mild break in a huge plain stretching for over six thousand miles from Germany to the Pacific Ocean, and partly because there is political sense in considering Russia (which, until about 1580, was confined to the region west of the Urals) part of Europe. Nevertheless, the Asian portion of Eurasia is so much larger than the European portion that Europe is often looked upon as a mere peninsula of Eurasia.

Africa is much more nearly a separate continent than Europe is. Its only land connection to Eurasia is the Suez Isthmus, which nowadays is about a hundred miles wide, and in ancient times was narrower.

Still the connection was there and it was a well-traveled one, with civilized men (and armies too) criss-crossing it now and again—whereas they rarely crossed the land north of the Black Sea. The Greeks were aware of the link between the nations they called Syria and Egypt, and they therefore considered Egypt and the land west of it to be a portion of Asia.

The matter was different to the Romans. They were farther from the Suez Isthmus and throughout their early history that connection was merely of academic interest to them. Their connection with Africa was entirely by way of the sea. Furthermore, as the Greeks had once faced Troy on opposing mainlands with the sea between, so—a thousand years later—the Romans faced the Carthaginians on opposing mainlands with the sea between. The struggle with Hannibal was every bit as momentous to the Romans as the struggle with Hector had been to the Greeks.

The Carthaginians called the region about their city by a word which, in Latin, became Africa. The word spread, in Roman consciousness, from the immediate neighborhood of Carthage (what is now northern Tunisia) to the entire mainland the Romans felt themselves to be facing. The geographers of Roman times, therefore—notably the Greek-Egyptian Ptolemy—granted Africa the dignity of being a third continent.

But let's face facts and ignore the accidents of history. If one ignores the Suez Canal, one can travel from the Cape of Good Hope to the Bering Strait, or to Portugal or Lapland, without crossing salt water, so that the whole body of land forms a single continent. This single continent has no generally accepted name and to call it "Eurafrasia," as I have sometimes felt the urge to do, is ridiculous.

We can think of it this way, though. This tract of land is enormous but it is finite and it is bounded on all sides by ocean. Therefore it is an island; a vast one, to be sure, but an island. If we take that into account then there is a name for it; one that is sometimes used by geopoliticians. It is "the World Island."

The name seems to imply that the triple continent of Europe-Asia-Africa makes up the whole world and, you know, it nearly does. Consider Table 14. (And let me

*Table 14—The World Island*

| | AREA (SQUARE MILES) | POPULATION |
|---|---|---|
| Asia | 16,500,000 | 1,580,000,000 |
| Africa | 11,500,000 | 290,000,000 |
| Europe | 3,800,000 | 640,000,000 |
| The World Island | 31,800,000 | 2,510,000,000 |

point out that in this and the succeeding tables in this article, the figures for area are good but those for population are often quite shaky. I have tried to choke mid-1960's population figures out of my library, but I haven't always been able to succeed. Furthermore, even when such figures are given they are all too frequently marked "estimate" and may be quite far off the truth. . . . But let's do our best.)

The World Island contains a little more than half the total land area of the globe. Even more significantly, it contains three-quarters of the Earth's population. It has a fair claim to the name.

The only tract of land that even faintly compares to the World Island in area and population is the American mainland, first discovered by primitive Asians many thousands of years ago, again by the Icelandic navigator Leif Ericsson in 1000 A.D., and finally by the Italian navigator Giovanni Caboto (John Cabot to the English nation, which employed his services) in 1497. . . . I don't mention Columbus because he discovered only islands prior to 1497. He did not touch the American mainland until 1498.

Columbus thought that the new mainland was part of Asia, and so indeed it might have been. Its complete physical independence of Asia was not demonstrated till 1728, when the Danish navigator Vitus Bering (employed by the Russians) explored what is now known as the Bering Sea and sailed through what is now called the Bering Strait, to show that Siberia and Alaska were not connected.

There is, therefore, a second immense island on Earth and this one is, traditionally, divided into two continents: North America and South America. These, however, if one ignores the man-made Panama Canal, are connected, and a man can travel from Alaska to Patagonia without crossing salt water.

There is no convenient name for the combined continents. It can be called "the Americas" but that makes use of a plural term for what is a single tract of land and I reject it for that reason.

I would like to suggest a name of my own—"the New World Island." This capitalizes on the common (if old-fashioned) phrase "the New World" for the Americas. It also indicates the same sort of relationship between the World Island and the New World Island that there is between England and New England, or between York and New York.

The vital statistics on the New World Island are presented in Table 15. As you see, the New World Island has about half the area of the World Island, but only a little over one-sixth the population.

*Table 15—The New World Island*

|  | AREA (SQUARE MILES) | POPULATION |
|---|---|---|
| North America | 9,385,000 | 275,000,000 |
| South America | 7,035,000 | 157,000,000 |
| The New World Island | 16,420,000 | 432,000,000 |

There are two other tracts of land large enough to be considered continents, and one tract which is borderline and is usually considered too small to be a continent. These are, in order of decreasing area; Antarctica (counting its ice cap), Australia, and Greenland.

Since Greenland is almost uninhabited, I would like (as a pure formality) to lump it in with the group of what we might call "continental-islands" just to get it out of the way. We can then turn to the bodies of land smaller than Greenland and concentrate on those as a group.

Table 16 lists the data on the continental-islands.

*Table 16—The Continental-Islands*

|  | AREA (SQUARE MILES) | POPULATION |
|---|---|---|
| The World Island | 31,800,000 | 2,510,000,000 |
| The New World Island | 16,420,000 | 432,000,000 |
| Antarctica | 5,100,000 | ............ |
| Australia | 2,970,000 | 11,000,000 |
| Greenland | 840,000 | 25,000 |

The bodies of land that remain—all smaller than Greenland—are what we usually refer to when we speak of "islands." From here on in, then, when I speak of "islands" in this essay, I mean bodies of land smaller than Greenland and entirely surrounded by the sea.

There are many thousands of such islands and they represent a portion of the land surface of the globe that is by no means negligible. Altogether (as nearly as I can estimate it) the islands have a total area of about 2,500,000 square miles—so that in combination they are continental in size, having almost the area of Australia. The total population is about 350,000,000, which is even more clearly continental in size, being well above the total population of North America.

Let's put it this way, one human being out of every ten lives on an island smaller than Greenland.

There are some useful statistics we can bring up in connection with the islands. First and most obvious is the matter of area. The five largest islands in terms of area are listed in Table 17.

*Table 17—The Largest Islands*

| | AREA (SQUARE MILES) |
|---|---|
| New Guinea | 312,329 |
| Borneo | 290,285 |
| Madagascar | 230,035 |
| Baffin | 201,600 |
| Sumatra | 163,145 |

The largest island, New Guinea, spreads out over an extreme length of 1,600 miles. If superimposed on the United States, it would stretch from New York to Denver. In area, it is fifteen percent larger than Texas. It has the largest and tallest mountain range outside those on the World Island and the New World Island, and some of the most primitive people in the world.

Two other islands of the first five are members of the same group as New Guinea. It, Borneo, and Sumatra are all part of what used to be called the "East Indies" an archipelago stretching across four thousand miles of ocean between Asia and Australia, and making up by far the largest island grouping in the world. The archipelago has an area of nearly one million square miles, and thus contains about forty percent of all the island area in the world. The archipelago bears a population of perhaps 103,000,000, or about thirty percent that of all the island population in the world.

In a way, Madagascar is like an East Indian island displaced four thousand miles westward to the other end of the Indian Ocean. It has roughly the shape of Sumatra and in size is midway between Sumatra and Borneo. Even its native population is more closely akin to those of Southeast Asia than to those of nearby Africa.

Only Baffin Island of the first giants falls outside this pattern. It is a member of the archipelago lying in the north of Canada. It is located between the mouth of Hudson Bay and the coast of Greenland.

Oddly enough, not one of the five largest islands is a giant in respect to population. There are three islands, indeed, (not one of which is among the five largest), which, among them, contain well over half of all the island people in the world. The most populous is probably not known by name to very many Americans. It is Honshu and, before you register a blank, let me explain that it is the largest of the Japanese islands, the one on which Tokyo is located.

The three islands are given in Table 18.

### Table 18—The Most Populous Islands

| | AREA | | POPULATION |
|---|---|---|---|
| | SQUARE MILES | RANK | |
| Honshu | 91,278 | 6 | 72,000,000 |
| Java | 48,504 | 12 | 66,000,000 |
| Great Britain | 88,133 | 7 | 54,000,000 |

Java is easily the most densely populated of the large islands. (I say "large islands" in order to exclude islands such as Manhattan.) It has a density of 1,350 people per square mile which makes it just eight times as densely populated as Europe. It is 1⅙ times as densely populated as Belgium, Europe's most thickly peopled nation. This is all the more remarkable since Belgium is highly industrialized and Java is largely agricultural. After all, one usually expects an industrialized area to support a larger population than an agricultural one would. (And, to be sure, Belgium's standard of living is much higher than Java's.)

Lagging far behind the big three are four other islands, each with more than ten million population. These are given in Table 19. (Kyushu, by the way, is another of the Japanese islands.)

*Table 19—The Moderately Populous Islands*

| | AREA | | POPULATION |
|---|---|---|---|
| | SQUARE MILES | RANK | |
| Kyushu | 14,791 | 30 | 13,000,000 |
| Sumatra | 163,145 | 5 | 12,500,000 |
| Formosa | 13,855 | 24 | 12,429,000 |
| Ceylon | 25,332 | 14 | 10,965,000 |

Notice that the seven most populous islands are all in the Eastern Hemisphere, all lying off the World Island or between the World Island and Australia. The most populous island of the Western Hemisphere is again one which most Americans probably can't name. It is Hispaniola, the island on which Haiti and the Dominican Republic are located. It's population is 8,200,000.

One generally thinks of great powers as located on the continents. All but one in history among the continental great powers were located on the World Island. (The one exception is the United States.)

The great exception to the rule of continentalism among the great powers is, of course, Great Britain.* In more recent times, Japan proved another. In fact, Great Britain and Japan are the only island nations that have been completely independent throughout medieval and modern history.

Nowadays, however (unless I have miscounted and I am sure that if I have I will be quickly enlightened by a number of Gentle Readers), there are no less than twenty-one island nations; twenty-one independent na-

---

*I'm not going to distinguish between England, Great Britain, the United Kingdom, and the British Isles. I can if I want to, though, never you fear!

tions, that is, whose territory is to be found on an island or group of islands, and who lack any significant base on either the World Island or the New World Island.

One of these nations, Australia, is actually a continent-nation by ordinary convention, but I'll include it here to be complete. The twenty-one island nations (including Australia) are listed in Table 20, in order of population.

### Table 20—The Island Nations

| | AREA | POPULATION |
|---|---|---|
| | (SQUARE MILES) | |
| Indonesia | 735,268 | 102,200,000 |
| Japan | 142,726 | 97,790,000 |
| Great Britain | 94,220 | 54,066,000 |
| Philippines | 115,707 | 32,629,000 |
| China, Nationalist | 13,885 | 12,429,000 |
| Australia | 2,971,021 | 11,313,000 |
| Ceylon | 25,332 | 10,965,000 |
| Cuba | 44,218 | 7,631,000 |
| Malagasy | 230,035 | 6,180,000 |
| Haiti | 10,714 | 4,660,000 |
| Dominican Republic | 18,816 | 3,573,000 |
| Ireland | 27,135 | 2,849,000 |
| New Zealand | 103,736 | 2,641,000 |
| Singapore | 224 | 1,844,000 |
| Jamaica | 4,232 | 1,745,000 |
| Trinidad and Tobago | 1,980 | 949,000 |
| Cyprus | 3,572 | 594,000 |
| Malta | 122 | 326,000 |
| Iceland | 39,768 | 190,230 |
| Western Samoa | 1,097 | 122,000 |
| Maldive Islands | 115 | 70,000 |

Some little explanatory points should accompany this table. First the discrepancy between Great Britain's area as an island and as a nation is caused by the fact that as a nation it includes certain regions outside its home island, notably Northern Ireland. Indonesia includes most but not all the archipelago I previously referred to as the East Indies. Nationalist China occupies the island of Formosa, and Malagasy occupies the island of Madagascar.

Virtually all the island people are now part of independent island nations. The largest islands (or parts of islands) I can think of that are still colonies in the old sense are the eastern half of New Guinea (pop. 2,000,000), which belongs to Australia; and Mauritius (pop. 721,000) and the Fiji Islands (pop. 435,000), which belong to Great Britain. I frankly don't know how to classify Puerto Rico. It is self-governing to a considerable extent but if it is counted as an American colony, I think it may qualify as the most populous (pop. 2,350,000) non-independent island remaining.

As you see from Table 20, the most populous island nation is neither Japan nor Great Britain, but Indonesia. It is, in fact, the fifth-most-populous nation in the world. Only China, India, the Soviet Union, and the United States (all giants in area) are more populous than Indonesia.

The only island nations that occupy less than a single island are Haiti and the Dominican Republic (which share Hispaniola) and Ireland, where the six northeastern counties are still part of Great Britain. The only island nation which has part of its islands belonging to nations based on some continent is Indonesia. Part of the island of Borneo (most of which is Indonesian) makes up a portion of the new nation of Malaysia, based on nearby Asia. The eastern half of New Guinea (the western half of which is Indonesian) belongs to Australia, and the northeastern half of the small Indonesian island of Timor belongs to Portugal.

Indonesia has another distinction. It is the only nation to have withdrawn voluntarily from the United Nations.

Western Samoa, on the other hand, is the only nation among those who have achieved independence since World War II to have voluntarily decided not to join the United Nations in the first place.

There are seventeen cities within these island nations which contain one million or more people. These are listed, in order of decreasing population, in Table 21— and I warn you that some of the figures are not particularly trustworthy.

### Table 21—The Island Cities

| CITY | NATION | POPULATION |
|------|--------|------------|
| Tokyo | Japan | 10,500,000 |
| London | Great Britain | 8,350,000 |
| Osaka | Japan | 3,196,000 |
| Djakarta | Indonesia | 2,975,000 |
| Sydney | Australia | 2,220,000 |
| Melbourne | Australia | 2,003,000 |
| Nagoya | Japan | 1,858,000 |
| Kobe | Japan | 1,180,000 |
| Yokohama | Japan | 1,585,000 |
| Havana | Cuba | 1,450,000 |
| Kyoto | Japan | 1,400,000 |
| Birmingham | Great Britain | 1,200,000 |
| Manila | Philippines | 1,140,000 |
| Surabaja | Indonesia | 1,135,000 |
| Glasgow | Great Britain | 1,020,000 |
| Bandung | Indonesia | 1,000,000 |
| Taipei | Nationalist China | 1,000,000 |

Of these, Tokyo is certainly remarkable since it may be the largest city in the world. I say "may be" because there is a second candidate for the post—Shanghai. Population statistics for the Chinese People's Republic (Communist China) are shaky indeed but there is a possibility that the population of Shanghai—a continental city—may be as high as 10,700,000, though figures as low as 7,000,000 are also given.

New York, the largest city on the New World Island, is no better than a good fourth, behind Tokyo, Shanghai, and Greater London. New York is located mostly on islands, of course. Only one of its boroughs, the Bronx, is indisputably on the mainland. Still it is not on an island in the same sense that Tokyo or London is.

If we exclude New York as a doubtful case, then the largest island city in the Western Hemisphere, and the only one in that half of the world to have a population of over a million, is Havana (though its population may recently have declined).

That leaves only one item. In restricting the discussion of islands to those which are surrounded by salt water, have we been forced to neglect any important fresh water islands?

In terms of size (rather than population) there is only one that is worth mentioning. It is a river island that very few in the world (outside Brazil) can be aware of it. It is the island of Marajó, which nestles like a huge basketball in the recess formed by the mouth of the Amazon River.

It is one hundred miles across and has an area of fourteen thousand square miles. It is larger than Formosa and if it were counted among the true islands of the sea it would be the thirty-third-largest island in the world, which is certainly not bad for a river island. However, it is a low-lying piece of land, swampy, often flooded, and right on the equator. Hardly anyone lives there.

Its mere existence, though, shows what a monster of a river the Amazon is. . . . But we're not discussing rivers now; perhaps another time.

# 5. FUTURE? TENSE!

ON THE WHOLE, there are two ways of looking at a science fiction writer.

One way is to consider him a nut. ("How are the little green men these days, Isaac?" "Been to the Moon lately, Ike, old boy?")

The other way is to consider him a keen-eyed viewer of the future. ("And what will the vacuum cleaner of the twenty-first century be like, Dr. Asimov?" "What sort of thing will be replacing television, Professor?")

Of the two, I suppose I prefer the former. It is, after all, quite easy to be a nut. I can do it on short notice anytime and anywhere, from faculty teas to science fiction conventions.

Predicting the future is a great deal more difficult, particularly on the terms usually set by those questioning you. What the questioners are invariably interested in are precise gadgetry details and that is exactly what I cannot give them.

You can well imagine, then, that when asked to address a sedate group, or write an article for a particularly staid periodical, the subject I least like to discuss is "The Future as I See It."

You can also well imagine that the subject I am asked to discuss, almost invariably, is—all right, you guessed it.

So I refuse! At least, I *usually* refuse. Unfortunately, although I am staunch and gimlet-eyed in my convictions and would far sooner die than compromise my principles, I have a weak point. I'm just an eentsy-weentsy bit susceptible to flattery.

Consequently, when the New York *Times* called, shortly after the New York World's Fair opened, and asked that I visit the Fair at their expense and write an article for them on what the world would be like fifty years or so in the future, I hesitated some, then agreed.

After all, I intended to visit the Fair anyway, and I expected to have a howling good time (and I *did*) and besides it was flattering to have the *Times* ask me and—

Well, anyway, I wrote the article and it appeared in the Sunday *Times* Magazine Section on August 16, 1964 (just in case all you Gentle Readers intend to make a mad dash for the library in order to read it).

Promptly, though, I paid the price of having swerved from my way of life, for the day after the article appeared, I got another flattering request to do a similar article for someone else. Then I received another flattering request to go on one of these conversation-type radio spots to answer telephoned questions from listeners ("Quick predictions on any subject off the top of your head, Dr. Asimov"), and so on. Naturally, I had to continue to accept flattering requests.

Yet if I don't make a tremendous effort to wrench loose, I may be tabbed for life as a keen-eyed infallible peerer into the future and the gentle joys of nut-dom may be forever withdrawn from me.

Perhaps I can lift the spell by using my rostrum here to describe my view of the predictive aspects of science fiction. Then people, getting the True View of it all, may stop asking me to play the uncongenial role of prophet.

To the outsider (that is, to the dweller beyond the pale, to whom the term "science fiction" conjures up fuzzy vistas of Flash Gordon and of Monsters from the Black Lagoon), the one serious aspect of science fiction is that it predicts things; and by this they usually mean that it predicts *specific* things.

The outsider, aware that science fiction writers wrote about atomic power decades before the Bomb was invented, imagines that those writers painstakingly described the theory of uranium fission. Or, knowing that science fiction writers have discussed trips to the Moon, imagines that those writers carefully included blueprints of three-stage rockets.

The fact is, however, that science fiction writers are invariably vague. The mere fact that I talk about positronic robots and say they are guided by the Three Laws of Robotics has no actual predictive value from the engineering standpoint. Imagine, for instance, a discussion between an interviewer (Q) and myself (A).

Q. What *is* a positronic robot, sir?

A. One with a positronic brain.

Q. And what is a positronic brain?

A. One in which positronic shifts take the place of the electronic shifts in the living human brain.

Q. But why should positronics be superior to electronics for the purpose?

A. I don't know.

Q. How do you keep your positrons from combining with electrons and forming a flood of energy that will melt down the robot into a puddle of metal?

A. I haven't the vaguest notion.

Q. For that matter, how do you translate positronic flows into the "Three Laws of Robotics"?

A. Beats me.

I am not ashamed of this. In writing my robot stories it is not my intention to describe robot-engineering in detail. It was merely my intention to describe a society in which advanced robots were common and to try to work out possible resulting consequences.

My focus was not on the specifics at all, but on generality.

Of course, a specific prediction may come true, but when it does, I am willing to bet that in virtually every case there is some extenuating circumstance that makes the prediction a non-prediction after all.

I can cite an example from among my own stories, but before I do that and proceed to antagonize all and sundry by seeming to hold myself up as a model, I wish to describe a case in which I fell lamentably and laughably short of predictive accuracy.

I once wrote a short story entitled "Everest," in which I explained man's failure to climb Mt. Everest by saying that its peak was occupied by a Martian observation party and that the Abominable Snowmen were really— yes, you guessed it.

I sold that story on April 7, 1953, and Mt. Everest was successfully climbed, with no signs of Martians, on May 29, 1953. (The story was published a half year later anyway.)

Now I can safely pass on to something that *sounds* like an accurate prediction. In my story "Super-Neutron" I have one character ask another if he remembers "the first atomic power plants of a hundred and seventy years ago and how they operated?"

"I believe," came the answer, "that they used the classical uranium fission method for power. They bombarded uranium with slow neutrons and split it up into masurium, barium, gamma rays, and more neutrons, thus establishing a cyclic process."

When I read this passage to people, nothing happens —until I show them that the issue of the magazine in which the story appeared is dated September 1941 and tell them it hit the stands in July 1941 and that the story was written in December 1940. This was two years *before* the first self-sustaining nuclear reactor was built and twelve years *before* the first nuclear power plant designed to produce electricity for civilian use was built.

To be sure, I wasn't able to predict that element number 43 was only called "masurium" temporarily, through a false-alarm discovery, and that when the element was *really* discovered it came to be called "technetium." In fact, it had been really discovered a couple of years before the story was written, but the new name given it had not yet reached me. Then, too, I didn't quite have the brains to say "chain reaction" instead of "cyclic process."

Even so, is it not an amazing prediction?

Nonsense! It wasn't prediction at all.

The story was written one year *after* uranium fission was discovered and announced. Once the announcement had been made, all talk about nuclear bombs and nuclear power plants was merely self-evident elaboration.

In early 1944, Cleve Cartmill's story "Deadline" appeared. It described the consequences of using an atomic bomb in such graphic correctness (a full year and a quarter *before* the first bomb was exploded at Alamogordo) that the FBI was alerted. And even that was not true prediction, but merely the self-evident elaboration of a known discovery.

My thesis is, in short, that it is *not* the details that are predicted; not the specific engineering points; not the gadgets; not the gimmicks. All predictions of that sort are either non-predictions or fortuitous strokes of luck and are, in any case, unimportant.

The broad vague brush with which the science fiction writer sketches the future is particularly suitable for the broad vague movements of social reaction. The science fiction writer is concerned with the broad sweeps of history, not the minutiae of gadgetry.

Let me give you an example of what I considered the greatest piece of true prediction ever to have appeared in any science fiction story. That story is "Solution Unsatisfactory" by Robert Heinlein (under his pseudonym of Anson MacDonald). It appeared in early 1941, over half a year before Pearl Harbor, and at a time when Hitler was at the high noon of his conquests.

The story dealt with the end of World War II and it

75

was wrong in many details. For instance, Heinlein did not manage to foresee Pearl Harbor and so the United States, in the story, remained at peace.

He did, however, forsee that the United States would organize a huge research program to develop a nuclear weapon. To be sure, it wasn't an atomic bomb that Heinlein had them invent but "atomic dust." (In a way, he skipped the Bomb and went on to fallout.)

Since Pearl Harbor had never happened (in the story), the atomic weapon was not used on Japanese cities, but on German ones. It ended the war and other nations (notably the Soviet Union) were kept from disturbing the peace further by the mere existence of the bomb in American hands.

But now, what was to be done with the weapon? The narrator of the story felt gleefully (even before the weapon had been used) that with this power in American hands, world peace would be enforced and the millennium would arrive in the form of a "Pax Americana."

But the hero of the story thinks otherwise. He says (and I hope Heinlein doesn't mind my quoting two paragraphs):

"Hmmm— I wish it were that easy. But it won't remain our secret; you can count on that. It doesn't matter how successfully we guard it; all that anyone needs is the hint given by the dust itself and then it is just a matter of time until some other nation develops a technique to produce it. You can't stop brains from working, John; the reinvention of the method is a mathematical certainty, once they know what it is they are looking for. And uranium is a common enough substance, widely distributed over the globe—don't forget that!

"It's like this: Once the secret is out—and it will be out if we ever use the stuff!—the whole world will be comparable to a room full of men, each armed with a loaded .45. They can't get out of the room and each

76

one is dependent on the good will of every other one to stay alive. All offense and no defense. See what I mean?"

What to do then? Consider Heinlein's title again: "Solution Unsatisfactory."

The point is that Heinlein predicted the nuclear stalemate that exists today, before the nuclear age had even opened. A full seven years after Heinlein had made his prediction, most American policy-makers still lulled themselves to sleep with the thought that we had a monopoly in the secret of the nuclear bomb that would last for generations because we alone had something called "Yankee know-how."

Not only is the nuclear stalemate harder to predict than the Bomb; it is the nuclear stalemate that is the important prediction. Think how much easier it was to produce the Bomb than it is proving to produce a safe way out of the nuclear stalemate. Think, therefore, how useful it would have been for policy-makers to have spent some time thinking of the consequences of the Bomb and not merely of the Bomb.

Science fiction performs its most useful function, then, not in predicting gadgets, but in predicting social consequences. In its task of predicting social consequences, it could be a tremendous force for human betterment.

Let me try to make this point even clearer by considering a hypothetical case. Pretend it is the year 1880 and that the automobile is the exciting gadget of the future that is being visualized by all science fiction writers. What kind of a story do you suppose might have been written, in 1880, around an automobile of the then future?

The automobile might have been viewed simply as a gadget. The story can be filled with all sorts of scientific gobbledygook describing the workings of the automobile. There could be the excitement of a last-minute failure in the framistan and the hero can be described as ingeniously designing a liebestraum out of an old baby carriage at the last minute and cleverly hooking it to the bispallator in such a way as to mutonate the karrogel.

(Of course, that's nonsense, but I can name you a number of stories written in that precise style, except that I won't because the authors are large-fisted, evil-tempered men.)

Another way is to view the automobile as a mere adjunct to adventure. Anything you can do on a horse you can do in an automobile, so you write a Western and go through it, crossing out "horse" and writing in "car."

You could then write, for instance: "The automobile came thundering down the stretch, its mighty tires pounding, and its tail assembly switching furiously from side to side, while its flaring foam-flecked air intake seemed rimmed with oil." Then, when the car has finally performed its task of rescuing the girl and confounding the bad guys, it sticks its fuel intake hose into a can of gasoline and quietly fuels itself.

Of course, I'm being satirical, but I wonder how far removed from reality this is. I'm willing to bet that lots of would-be science fiction writers start stories as follows: "The spaceship skidded to a halt five million miles outside Venus, its brake linings scorched and squealing."

The only reason we don't see such stories is that editors see them first.

Obviously, writing a science fiction story in which an automobile is nothing more than a gadget, or merely a superhorse, is a waste of time. Oh, it may make an honest dollar for the writer and it may give the reader an hour's honest amusement, but where is its importance? It has "predicted the automobile," yes, but predicting the mere existence of the automobile is *nothing*.

What about the effect of the automobile on society and on people? After all it is *people* that interest people.

For instance, suppose you consider the automobile as an object turned out by the millions for the use of anyone who cares to buy one. (You are still in 1880, remember!) Imagine a whole population placed on wheels.

Won't cities spread out since no one will have to live immediately next to his place of business? He can live twenty miles away yet go scooting in each morning and out each evening. In short, won't cities be suburbanized while their centers fall into decay?

And if you have millions of cars, won't you have to criss-cross the nation with highways? And how will that affect vacation habits? And status-seeking? And the railroads? And if youngsters can drive off somewhere in cars, how will that affect the status of youth? Of sex? Of women?

You may think, of course, that it is easy to look back on the pre-automobile age from the present and talk about what must come. And I must admit that I take a back seat to no one in the unerring clarity of my hindsight.

But foresight is not completely impossible, either. Back in 1901, H. G. Wells, with the automobile age merely beginning, wrote a book entitled "Anticipations of the Reaction of Mechanical and Scientific Progress upon Human Life and Thought" in which, among other things, he described the modern motor age with astonishing accuracy.

Very well, then, you are going to write a science fiction story in 1880 about the automobile and you are going to do something less trivial than merely to predict the automobile. You are going to pick your plot out of the fascinating changes the automobile is going to bring to society. What's more, you'll pick one of the few changes that even H. G. Wells didn't anticipate.

Let's start— You have your motorized society. Every head of a family has a car; some have two. Every morning several hundred thousand cars enter the city from its ring of suburbs; every evening several hundred thousand cars return. The city becomes a giant organism, inhaling cars every morning, exhaling cars every evening.

Very good so far. Now we have our hero—ordinary chap, clean-cut, wife, two children, sense of humor, excellent driver. He's being inhaled by the city. There he is, moving along into the city with many, many other cars; all moving in; all converging—

Aha! And when all the cars get into the city, where do they go?

That's it! That's it! There's the title of the story: "Crunch!" The contents? A delightful satire about our hero spending all day looking for a parking spot and, in the process, meeting traffic jams, taxi drivers, traffic cops, trucks, parking meters, filled garages, fire hydrants, etc., etc.

A delightful satire, that is, in 1880. At present, it would bear more of the nature of stark, realistic tragedy.

Consider now:

If such a story had actually been written in 1880 and had caught on thoroughly enough to have interested policy-makers, would it not have been just barely possible that city growth from 1880 on might have been directed with an eventual motor civilization in mind?

Think of it, oh, those of you who live in northeastern cities such as New York or Boston, which have been cleverly designed for nothing more elaborate than the pushcart, and tell me what reward would be sufficient for the writer who had performed such a service.

Do you see, then, that the important prediction is not the automobile, but the parking problem; not radio, but the soap opera; not the income tax, but the expense account; not the Bomb, but the nuclear stalemate? Not the action, in short, but the reaction?

Of course, to expect the men of 1880 to have planned cities for an eventual motorized society is perhaps to expect too much of human nature. I wonder, though, if to expect the equivalent today may not be expecting barely enough.

For a century now, we've been watching social changes take place at an ever increasing pace and have been watching ourselves being caught flat-footed with consequences of ever increasing dislocation.

By now, we've learned to expect change, even drastic change, and we are resigning ourselves to the necessity of anticipating, of planning in advance.

The very existence and popularity of science fiction is an indication of how the inevitability of change is coming to be accepted. And one of the functions of science fiction is to make the fact of change less unpalatable to the average human being.

No matter how much the general populace ignored science fiction and laughed at it, they could not remain completely unaware of its contents. Some of its subject matter seeped into the general consciousness, even if only by way of greatly diluted and distorted comic strips. For that reason the coming of nuclear weapons, of missiles, of man-made satellites did not meet with the psychological resistance they might have once.

Well, then, enough of the past. We're in the present and the task of the science fiction writer lies in considering the future—the real future of now, not the hindsight one of 1880.

We are in the midst of at least four sets of first-class revolutionary changes, each of which is following a clear and inevitable path. What will the reaction be to each of these sets of changes?

The first and most frightening is the "population explosion," and science fiction has considered that in a number of ways. I can think of a number of stories set against the background of a drastically overpopulated Earth. "The Caves of Steel" is an example from among my own stories and another is "Gravy Planet" ("Space Merchants") by Frederick Pohl and Cyril Kornbluth.

The most savage and effective story of this sort (at

least, in my opinion) was Frederick Pohl's "The Census Takers," in which population was held at a desirable level by the simple device of taking a world census every ten years and shooting every thirteenth individual counted. . . . Or fifteenth or ninth, or whatever fraction was estimated as being required.

This is "anti-prediction" if I may coin a term. Fred Pohl obviously didn't think this was going to happen. He knew—we all know—that such a solution is unthinkable.

But the anti-prediction of an impossibility has its uses, too. By its sheer shock value it may force people who are only too prone to solve the insoluble by ignoring it to stop and think. All right, we *don't* shoot the surplus at random. What alternative, then, is there?

Another revolutionary change is the "automation explosion." That, of course, involves the rapid arrival of a world equivalent to that familiar science fiction situation in which all manual labor and much of the mental labor is done by robots. What happens to mankind in that case? Karl Capek took up that problem in "R.U.R." as long ago as 1921. A more recent example is Jack Williamson's "With Folded Hands—"

What kind of a world will we live in, anyway, when meaningful work becomes a luxury available only to the few; when boredom becomes a worldwide disease. Can times become even more neurotic than they are now? Well, read "Coming Attraction" by Fritz Leiber on our neurotic future.

A third revolutionary change is the "information explosion," for scientific discoveries are coming so thickly and quickly that the human mind has become incapable of grasping, in full depth, more than an extremely narrow specialty.

My own attempt in this direction was a story called "Dead Hand" in which I postulated the existence of professional science writers who winnowed out the scientific work of others and then wrote papers that were concise and clear. They served, furthermore, as the bridge across the specialties, with the broad, cross-disciplinary (if superficial) knowledge.

A fourth major change is the "freedom explosion," the emergence of the erstwhile colonies, the revolution of the "natives"—and the concomitant civil rights movement within the United States.

Science fiction writers have not, perhaps, worked at this as thoroughly as upon the others. Ray Bradbury had an excellent story called, if memory serves me, "Way in the Middle of the Air" about the effect upon the United States of a mass migration of Negroes to Mars. I, myself, somewhat more realistically, viewed the emergence of an independent Africa in my story "The Evitable Conflict" (published in 1950, by the way, well before the fact). Then, too, in my novel *The Currents of Space* I dealt—but not very explicitly, I must admit—with the role of the Negro in the colonization of the Galaxy.

Anyway, these are some of the major changes we are facing, each one of which will suffice to disrupt the world we know, before a single generation has passed. If the disruption is to be kept from turning into disintegration, we must make intelligent guesses as to where we're going and act upon them *now*.

It is the function of the science fiction writer (aside from earning a living and pleasing his readers) to make those guesses, and that makes him the most important servant (in my opinion) that humanity now possesses.

To be sure, the science fiction writer is no longer the only one making such guesses. Matters have progressed to the point where various government agencies, research institutions, and industrial concerns are desperately trying to peer into the clouded crystal ball. But it's my personal guess that nearly every man in government or industry who is so engaged was at one time or another a science fiction reader.

—So now look what I've done. I started the chapter with the intention of complaining about having to write these difficult articles of prediction and I end by convincing myself I ought to write more of them.

Apparently, I wasn't able to predict the end of this chapter when I began it.

So much for my predictive ability.

# 6. THE NOBELMEN OF SCIENCE

SOMETHING HAPPENED TO ME some time ago which still leaves me stunned.

I got a call early in the morning from a reporter. He said, "Three Frenchmen have just won the Nobel Prize for Medicine and Physiology for their work on genetics, and I thought you might explain to me, in simple terms, the significanec of their discoveries."

"Who are the three Frenchmen?" I asked.

He told me, and the names drew a blank. I pleaded ignorance of their work and apologized. He hung up.

I sat there for a while and brooded, since I hate revealing flaws in my omniscience. As is usual in such cases, I thought long, shivery thoughts about the on-coming of senility, and then cudgeled my brain un-mercifully. What discoveries in genetics in recent years, I wondered, would rate a Nobel Prize this year?

One thought came to mind. Some years back it had been discovered that mongolism (a kind of congenital mental retardation marked by a variety of characteristic symptoms) was accompanied by an additional chromo-some in the cells. The twenty-first pair had three mem-bers rather than two, giving a total number of forty-seven rather than forty-six.

I ripped into my library to find the record of the discovery and came upon it in a matter of minutes. Eureka! It had first been reported by three Frenchmen!

My chest expanded; my cheeks glowed; my brain palpitated. There was life, it seemed, in the old boy yet.

I called the reporter back, savoring my triumph in advance, "What were the names of those Frenchmen, again?" I asked cheerfully.

He rattled them off. *They were three different names!* There was a long dismal pause, and then I said, "Sorry, I still don't know."

He must be wondering, ever since, why I bothered calling him back. As for me, I faced the situation staunchly; I got back into bed and pulled the covers over my head.

(If you're curious, the three Frenchmen who won the 1965 prize—who will be named later in the article— received it for the discovery that some genes have regulatory functions and control the activity of other genes.)

It got me to thinking about Nobel Prize winners, however, and the way such victories have become a matter of national pride. After all, the reporter didn't identify the winners as "three geneticists" but as "three Frenchmen."

But in what way ought nations to take credit? Einstein, for instance, was born in Germany, but was educated in Italy and Switzerland as well as in Germany, was in Germany at the time he won the award, though he was in Switzerland at the time he wrote his first world-shattering papers, and he spent his later life as an American citizen. How do we list him?

I would like to suggest that the key point is a man's scientific birth and that this takes place in college. Schooling before college is too vague and diffuse, schooling after college involves a man who is already set in his directions. It is college itself that sets those directions and determines whether a man will throw himself into science or not.

Naturally, I am aware that influences prior to college and outside college may be very important but here we edge uncomfortably close to the task of making a psychiatric study of each Nobel Prize winner, which I can't and won't do. I am going to accept college as a "first approximation" and list the winners by the nationality of that college.

This isn't easy, either.

In the first place, the information I can dig up isn't always clear in this matter and I may make some mistakes. Secondly, some Nobelists went to two different undergraduate colleges in two different nations and I have to choose among them. Thirdly, deciding on a nationality brings me face to face with the fact that political divisions change their nature with time. Some colleges that were once located in Austria-Hungary are now located in Czechoslovakia, without having ever budged.

One Nobel Prize winner studied at the University of Dorpat, and this is perhaps the most troublesome case. The university was in Russia then and it is in the Soviet Union now. In between, however, it was in Estonia, which the American government still recognizes as an independent nation. And to top it off, I'm sure that both the winner himself and the university, in his time, were completely German in a cultural sense.

Oh, well, I will take full responsibility for my decisions on categories and I am certain that those Gentle Readers who take issue with those decisions will write me and tell me so. And I may be argued into making changes.

So now let's make the lists which, if they make dull reading, have the advantage of not being like any other list in existence (as far as I know) and which therefore come under the heading, I hope, of "valuable reference."

We'll start with the Nobel Prize in physics in Table 22:

*Table 22—The Physics Nobelists*

| YEAR | WINNER(S)—PHYSICS | UNDERGRADUATE TRAINING |
|------|-------------------|------------------------|
| 1901 | Wilhelm Konrad Röntgen | Switzerland |
| 1902 | Hendrik Antoon Lorentz | Netherlands |
|      | Pieter Zeeman | Netherlands |
| 1903 | Antoine Henri Becquerel | France |
|      | Pierre Curie | France |
|      | Marie Sklodowska Curie | France |
| 1904 | John William Strutt, Baron Rayleigh | Great Britain |
| 1905 | Philipp Lenard | Austria |
| 1906 | Joseph John Thomson | Great Britain |
| 1907 | Albert Abraham Michelson | United States |
| 1908 | Gabriel Lippmann | France |
| 1909 | Guglielmo Marconi | Italy (private tutoring) |
|      | Carl Ferdinand Braun | Germany |
| 1910 | Johannes Diderik Van der Waals | Netherlands |
| 1911 | Wilhelm Wien | Germany |
| 1912 | Nils Gustaf Dalén | Sweden |
| 1913 | Heike Kamerlingh Onnes | Netherlands |
| 1914 | Max Theodor Felix von Laue | Germany |
| 1915 | William Henry Bragg | Great Britain |
|      | William Lawrence Bragg | Australia |
| 1916 | (no award) | |
| 1917 | Charles Glover Barkla | Great Britain |
| 1918 | Max Karl Ernst Ludwig Planck | Germany |
| 1919 | Johannes Stark | Germany |
| 1920 | Charles Edouard Guillaume | Switzerland |
| 1921 | Albert Einstein | Switzerland |
| 1922 | Niels Henrik David Bohr | Denmark |
| 1923 | Robert Andrews Millikan | United States |
| 1924 | Karl Manne Georg Siegbahn | Sweden |
| 1925 | James Franck | Germany |
|      | Gustav Hertz | Germany |
| 1926 | Jean Perrin | France |
| 1927 | Arthur Holly Compton | United States |
|      | Charles Thomson Rees Wilson | Great Britain |
| 1928 | Owen Willans Richardson | Great Britain |

| YEAR | WINNER(S)—PHYSICS | UNDERGRADUATE TRAINING |
|---|---|---|
| 1929 | Prince Louis-Victor de Broglie | France |
| 1930 | Chandrasekhara Venkata Raman | India |
| 1931 | (no award) | |
| 1932 | Werner Karl Heisenberg | Germany |
| 1933 | Erwin Schrödinger | Austria |
| | Paul Adrien Maurice Dirac | Great Britain |
| 1934 | (no award) | |
| 1935 | James Chadwick | Great Britain |
| 1936 | Victor Francis Hess | Austria |
| | Carl David Anderson | United States |
| 1937 | Clinton Joseph Davisson | United States |
| | George Paget Thomson | Great Britain |
| 1938 | Enrico Fermi | Italy |
| 1939 | Ernest Orlando Lawrence | United States |
| 1940 | (no award) | |
| 1941 | (no award) | |
| 1942 | (no award) | |
| 1943 | Otto Stern | Germany |
| 1944 | Isidor Isaac Rabi | United States |
| 1945 | Wolfgang Pauli | Austria |
| 1946 | Percy Williams Bridgman | United States |
| 1947 | Edward Victor Appleton | Great Britain |
| 1948 | Patrick Maynard Stuart Blackett | Great Britain |
| 1949 | Hideki Yukawa | Japan |
| 1950 | Cecil Frank Powell | Great Britain |
| 1951 | John Douglas Cockcroft | Great Britain |
| | Ernest Thomas Sinton Walton | Ireland |
| 1952 | Felix Bloch | Switzerland |
| | Edward Mills Purcell | United States |
| 1953 | Fritz Zernike | Netherlands |
| 1954 | Max Born | Germany |
| | Walter Bothe | Germany |
| 1955 | Willis Eugene Lamb, Jr. | United States |
| | Polykarp Kusch | United States |
| 1956 | William Bradford Shockley | United States |
| | John Bardeen | United States |
| | Walter Houser Brattain | United States |

| YEAR | WINNER(S)—PHYSICS | UNDERGRADUATE TRAINING |
|------|-------------------|------------------------|
| 1957 | Tsung-Dao Lee | China |
| | Chen-Ning Yang | China |
| 1958 | Pavel Alekseyevich Cherenkov | Soviet Union |
| | Ilya Mihailovich Frank | Soviet Union |
| | Igor Yevgenyevich Tamm | Soviet Union |
| 1959 | Emilio Segrè | Italy |
| | Owen Chamberlain | United States |
| 1960 | Donald Arthur Glaser | United States |
| 1961 | Robert Hofstadter | United States |
| | Rudolf Ludwig Mössbauer | Germany |
| 1962 | Lev Davidovich Landau | Soviet Union |
| 1963 | Eugene Wigner | Germany |
| | J. Hans Daniel Jensen | Germany |
| | Maria Goeppert-Mayer | Germany |
| 1964 | Charles Hard Townes | United States |
| | Nikolai Basov | Soviet Union |
| | Alexander Prokhorov | Soviet Union |
| 1965 | Julian Seymour Schwinger | United States |
| | Richard Phillips Feynman | United States |
| | Shinichero Tomonago | Japan |

Next we'll take up the Nobel Prizes in chemistry in Table 23:

*Table 23—The Chemistry Nobelists*

| YEAR | WINNER(S)—CHEMISTRY | UNDERGRADUATE TRAINING |
|------|---------------------|------------------------|
| 1901 | Jacobus Henricus Van't Hoff | Netherlands |
| 1902 | Emil Fischer | Germany |
| 1903 | Svante August Arrhenius | Sweden |
| 1904 | William Ramsay | Great Britain |
| 1905 | Adolf von Baeyer | Germany |
| 1906 | Henri Moissan | France |
| 1907 | Eduard Buchner | Germany |
| 1908 | Ernest Rutherford | New Zealand |
| 1909 | Wilhelm Ostwald | Russia |
| 1910 | Otto Wallach | Germany |

| YEAR | WINNER(S)—CHEMISTRY | UNDERGRADUATE TRAINING |
|---|---|---|
| 1911 | Marie Sklodowska Curie | France |
| 1912 | Victor Grignard | France |
|  | Paul Sabatier | France |
| 1913 | Alfred Werner | Switzerland |
| 1914 | Theodore William Richards | United States |
| 1915 | Richard Willstätter | Germany |
| 1916 | (no award) | |
| 1917 | (no award) | |
| 1918 | Fritz Haber | Germany |
| 1919 | (no award) | |
| 1920 | Walther Nernst | Germany |
| 1921 | Frederick Soddy | Great Britain |
| 1922 | Francis William Aston | Great Britain |
| 1923 | Fritz Pregl | Austria |
| 1924 | (no award) | |
| 1925 | Richard Zsigmondy | Austria |
| 1926 | Theodor Svedberg | Sweden |
| 1927 | Heinrich Wieland | Germany |
| 1928 | Adolf Windaus | Germany |
| 1929 | Arthur Harden | Great Britain |
|  | Hans von Euler-Chelpin | Germany |
| 1930 | Hans Fischer | Germany |
| 1931 | Carl Bosch | Germany |
|  | Friedrich Bergius | Germany |
| 1932 | Irving Langmuir | United States |
| 1933 | (no award) | |
| 1934 | Harold Clayton Urey | United States |
| 1935 | Irène Joliot-Curie | France |
|  | Frédéric Joliot-Curie | France |
| 1936 | Peter Joseph Wilhelm Debye | Germany |
| 1937 | Walter Norman Haworth | Great Britain |
|  | Paul Karrer | Switzerland |
| 1938 | Richard Kuhn | Germany |
| 1939 | Adolf Butenandt | Germany |
|  | Leopold Ruzicka | Switzerland |
| 1940 | (no award) | |

| YEAR | WINNER(S)—CHEMISTRY | UNDERGRADUATE TRAINING |
|---|---|---|
| 1941 | (no award) | |
| 1942 | (no award) | |
| 1943 | Georg von Hevesy | Hungary |
| 1944 | Otto Hahn | Germany |
| 1945 | Artturi Ilmari Virtanen | Finland |
| 1946 | James Batcheller Sumner | United States |
| | John Howard Northrop | United States |
| | Wendell Meredith Stanley | United States |
| 1947 | Robert Robinson | Great Britain |
| 1948 | Arne Tiselius | Sweden |
| 1949 | William Francis Giauque | United States |
| 1950 | Otto Diels | Germany |
| | Kurt Alder | Germany |
| 1951 | Glenn Theodore Seaborg | United States |
| | Edwin Mattison McMillan | United States |
| 1952 | Archer John Porter Martin | Great Britain |
| | Richard Laurence Millington Synge | Great Britain |
| 1953 | Hermann Staudinger | Germany |
| 1954 | Linus Pauling | United States |
| 1955 | Vincent Du Vigneaud | United States |
| 1956 | Cyril Norman Hinshelwood | Great Britain |
| | Nikolai Nikolaevitch Semënov | Soviet Union |
| 1957 | Alexander Robertus Todd | Great Britain |
| 1958 | Frederick Sanger | Great Britain |
| 1959 | Jaroslav Heyrovsky | Czechoslovakia |
| 1960 | Willard Frank Libby | United States |
| 1961 | Melvin Calvin | United States |
| 1962 | Max Ferdinand Perutz | Austria |
| | John Cowdery Kendrew | Great Britain |
| 1963 | Karl Ziegler | Germany |
| | Giulio Natta | Italy |
| 1964 | Dorothy Crowfoot Hodgkin | Great Britain |
| 1965 | Robert Burns Woodward | United States |

Finally, the Nobel Prizes for medicine and physiology in Table 24:

Table 24—*The Physiology Nobelists*

| YEAR | WINNER(S)—MED. AND PHYSIOL. | UNDERGRADUATE TRAINING |
|---|---|---|
| 1901 | Emil von Behring | Germany |
| 1902 | Ronald Ross | Great Britain |
| 1903 | Niels Ryberg Finsen | Denmark |
| 1904 | Ivan Petrovich Pavlov | Russia |
| 1905 | Robert Koch | Germany |
| 1906 | Camillo Golgi | Italy |
|  | Santiago Ramón y Cajal | Spain |
| 1907 | Charles Louis Alphonse Laveran | France |
| 1908 | Ilya Mechnikov | Russia |
|  | Paul Ehrlich | Germany |
| 1909 | Theodor Kocher | Switzerland |
| 1910 | Albrecht Kossel | Germany |
| 1911 | Allvar Gullstrand | Sweden |
| 1912 | Alexis Carrel | France |
| 1913 | Charles Richet | France |
| 1914 | Robert Bárány | Austria |
| 1915 | (no award) | |
| 1916 | (no award) | |
| 1917 | (no award) | |
| 1918 | (no award) | |
| 1919 | Jules Bordet | Belgium |
| 1920 | August Krogh | Denmark |
| 1921 | (no award) | |
| 1922 | Archibald Vivian Hill | Great Britain |
|  | Otto Meyerhof | Germany |
| 1923 | Frederick Grant Banting | Canada |
|  | John James Richard Macleod | Great Britain |
| 1924 | Willem Einthoven | Netherlands |
| 1925 | (no award) | |
| 1926 | Johannes Fibiger | Denmark |
| 1927 | Julius Wagner-Jauregg | Austria |
| 1928 | Charles Nicolle | France |
| 1929 | Christiaan Eijkman | Netherlands |
|  | Frederick Gowland Hopkins | Great Britain |
| 1930 | Karl Landsteiner | Austria |

| YEAR | WINNER(S)—MED. AND PHYSIOL. | UNDERGRADUATE TRAINING |
|------|------------------------------|-------------------------|
| 1931 | Otto Warburg | Germany |
| 1932 | Charles Sherrington | Great Britain |
|      | Edgar Douglas Adrian | Great Britain |
| 1933 | Thomas Hunt Morgan | United States |
| 1934 | George Hoyt Whipple | United States |
|      | George Richards Minot | United States |
|      | William Parry Murphy | United States |
| 1935 | Hans Spemann | Germany |
| 1936 | Henry Dale | Great Britain |
|      | Otto Loewi | Germany |
| 1937 | Albert von Szent-Györgyi | Hungary |
| 1938 | Corneille Heymans | Belgium |
| 1939 | Gerhard Domagk | Germany |
| 1940 | (no award) | |
| 1941 | (no award) | |
| 1942 | (no award) | |
| 1943 | Henrik Dam | Denmark |
|      | Edward A. Doisy | United States |
| 1944 | Joseph Erlanger | United States |
|      | Herbert Spencer Gasser | United States |
| 1945 | Alexander Fleming | Great Britain |
|      | Ernst Boris Chain | Germany |
|      | Howard Walter Florey | Australia |
| 1946 | Hermann Joseph Muller | United States |
| 1947 | Bernardo Alberto Houssay | Argentina |
|      | Carl Ferdinand Cori | Czechoslovakia |
|      | Gerty Theresa Radnitz Cori | Czechoslovakia |
| 1948 | Paul Müller | Switzerland |
| 1949 | Walter Rudolf Hess | Switzerland |
|      | Egas Moniz | Portugal |
| 1950 | Edward Calvin Kendall | United States |
|      | Philip Showalter Hench | United States |
|      | Tadeus Reichstein | Switzerland |
| 1951 | Max Theiler | South Africa |
| 1952 | Selman Abraham Waksman | United States |
| 1953 | Fritz Albert Lipmann | Germany |
|      | Hans Adolf Krebs | Germany |

| YEAR | WINNER(S)—MED. AND PHYSIOL. | UNDERGRADUATE TRAINING |
|---|---|---|
| 1954 | John Franklin Enders | United States |
| | Thomas Huckle Weller | United States |
| | Frederick Chapman Robbins | United States |
| 1955 | Axel Hugo Teodor Theorell | Sweden |
| 1956 | Dickinson Woodruff Richards | United States |
| | André Frédéric Cournand | France |
| | Werner Theodor Otto Forssmann | Germany |
| 1957 | Daniel Bovet | Switzerland |
| 1958 | George Wells Beadle | United States |
| | Edward Lawrie Tatum | United States |
| | Joshua Lederberg | United States |
| 1959 | Severo Ochoa | Spain |
| | Arthur Kornberg | United States |
| 1960 | Macfarlane Burnet | Australia |
| | Peter Brian Medawar | Great Britain |
| 1961 | George von Bekesy | Switzerland |
| 1962 | Francis Harry Compton Crick | Great Britain |
| | Maurice Hugh Frederick Wilkins | Great Britain |
| | James Dewey Watson | United States |
| 1963 | John Carew Eccles | Australia |
| | Alan Lloyd Hodgkin | Great Britain |
| | Andrew Fielding Huxley | Great Britain |
| 1964 | Konrad Bloch | Germany |
| | Feodor Lynen | Germany |
| 1965 | André Lwoff | France |
| | Jacques Monod | France |
| | François Jacob | France |

Now for some overall statistics—50 physics prizes have been shared among 86 people (including 2 women); 57 chemistry prizes have been shared among 71 people (including 3 women); 56 medicine and physiology prizes have been shared among 90 people (including 1 woman).

All told, 246 people (including 5 women) have won among them a total of 172 prizes in the sciences through 1965. (If this sum seems wrong to you, I must remind you that Marie Sklodowska Curie won two science prizes, one in physics and one in chemistry.)

Suppose we next list the prizes according to the college nationality of the winners. In making this final table, I will give half-credit to each man who shares the prize with one other and third-credit to each man who shares the prize with two others. Sometimes the cash award of the prize is divided ½, ¼, and ¼, but I'll ignore that refinement.

The result follows in Table 25.

### Table 25—Nobelists by Nationality

| NATION | PHYSICS | CHEMISTRY | MEDICINE & PHYSIOLOGY | TOTAL |
|---|---|---|---|---|
| Germany | 10 | 17½ | 10⅙ | 37⅔ |
| United States | 12 | 11 | 9⅙ | 32⅙ |
| Great Britain | 10½ | 10 | 6⅙ | 26⅔ |
| France | 4 | 4 | 5½ | 13½ |
| Switzerland | 3½ | 2 | 4⅚ | 10⅓ |
| Austria | 3 | 2½ | 3 | 8½ |
| Sweden | 2 | 3 | 2 | 7 |
| Netherlands | 4 | 1 | 1½ | 6½ |
| Soviet Union (Russia) | 2⅔ | 1½ | 1½ | 5⅔ |
| Denmark | 1 | — | 3½ | 4½ |
| Italy | 2 | ½ | ½ | 3 |
| Hungary | — | 1 | 1 | 2 |
| Belgium | — | — | 2 | 2 |
| Australia | ½ | — | 1⅙ | 1⅔ |
| Czechoslovakia | — | 1 | ⅔ | 1⅔ |
| Japan | 1⅓ | — | — | 1⅓ |
| India | 1 | — | — | 1 |
| China | 1 | — | — | 1 |
| New Zealand | — | 1 | — | 1 |
| Finland | — | 1 | — | 1 |
| Spain | — | — | 1 | 1 |
| South Africa | — | — | 1 | 1 |
| Ireland | ½ | — | — | ½ |
| Portugal | — | — | ½ | ½ |
| Canada | — | — | ½ | ½ |
| Argentina | — | — | ⅓ | ⅓ |
| Totals | 59 | 57 | 56 | 172 |

Too much must not be read into this table. It can't and should not be used to indicate anything about the relative intelligences of the nations. There is a wide difference in quality between one Nobelist and another and these differences are impossible to weigh objectively. For instance, Italy has a score of only 3 altogether, but one of those three was scored by Enrico Fermi. Denmark only has 1 physics prize to its credit, but that one was Niels Bohr, a giant even among giants.

What the table does show is that the scientific tradition has been entrenched longest and most strongly in the educational systems of those nations culturally related to Great Britain and Germany. As nearly as I can estimate colleges that teach in either English, German, Swedish, Dutch, or Danish account for 135⅔, or 80 percent, of the Nobel Prizes in the sciences.

I suspect that this English-German domination of science will grow progressively less marked in succeeding decades.

And I would like to make one final pitch, too. It is about time that the arbitrary decision of Nobel that only three classifications of science deserve the prize be reconsidered. I'm thinking of three more classifications: a) Astronomy (to include geology and oceanography), b) Mathematics, and c) Science of man (to include anthropology, psychology, and, possibly, sociology).

Many great scientists go unhonored by the present system and it bothers me. (And it probably bothers them, too.)

# PART II

## — TO —

# 7. EXCLAMATION POINT!

IT IS A SAD THING to be unrequitedly in love, I can tell you. The truth is that I love mathematics and mathematics is completely indifferent to me.

Oh, I can handle the elementary aspects of math all right but as soon as subtle insights are required, she goes in search of someone else. She's not interested in me.

I know this because every once in a while I get all involved with pencil and paper, on the track of some great mathematical discovery and so far I have obtained only two kinds of results: 1) completely correct findings that are quite old, and 2) completely new findings that are quite wrong.

For instance (as an example of the first class of results), I discovered, when I was very young, that the sums of successive odd numbers were successive squares. In other words: $1=1$; $1+3=4$; $1+3+5=9$; $1+3+5+7=16$, and so on. Unfortunately, Pythagoras knew this too in 500 B.C., and I suspect that some Babylonian knew it in 1500 B.C.

An example of the second kind of result involves Fermat's Last Theorem.* I was thinking about it a couple of months ago when a sudden flash of insight struck me and a kind of luminous glow irradiated the interior of my skull. *I was able to prove the truth of Fermat's Last Theorem in a very simple way.*

***

*I'm not going to discuss that here. Suffice it to say now that it is the most famous unsolved problem in mathematics.

When I tell you that the greatest mathematicians of the last three centuries have tackled Fermat's Last Theorem with ever increasingly sophisticated mathematical tools and that all have failed, you will realize what a stroke of unparalleled genius it was for me to succeed with nothing more than ordinary arithmetical reasoning.

My delirium of ecstasy did not completely blind me to the fact that my proof depended upon one assumption which I could check very easily with pencil and paper. I went upstairs to my study to carry that check through —stepping very carefully so as not to jar all that brilliance inside my cranium.

You guessed it, I'm sure. My assumption proved to be quite false inside of a few minutes. Fermat's Last Theorem was not proven after all; and my radiance paled into the light of ordinary day as I sat at my desk, disappointed and miserable.

Now that I have recovered completely, however, I look back on that episode with some satisfaction. After all, for five minutes, I was *convinced* that I was soon to be recognized as the most famous living mathematician in the world, and words cannot express how wonderful that felt while it lasted!

On the whole, though, I suppose that true old findings, however minor, are better than new false ones, however major. So I will trot out for your delectation, a little discovery of mine which I made just the other day but which, I am certain, is over three centuries old in reality.

However, I've never seen it anywhere, so until some Gentle Reader writes to tell me who first pointed it out and when, I will adopt the discovery as the Asimov Series.

First, let me lay the groundwork.

We can begin with the following expression; $(1+1/n)^n$ where $n$ can be set equal to any whole number. Suppose we try out a few numbers.

If $n=1$, the expression becomes $(1+\frac{1}{1})^1=2$. If $n=2$, the expression becomes $(1+\frac{1}{2})^2$ or $(\frac{3}{2})^2$ or $\frac{9}{4}$ or 2.25. If $n=3$, the expression becomes $(1+\frac{1}{3})^3$ or $(\frac{4}{3})^3$ or $\frac{64}{27}$ or about 2.3074.

We can prepare Table 26 of the value of the expression for a selection of various values of $n$:

*Table 26—*

| N | $(1+1/N)^n$ |
|---|---|
| 1 | 2 |
| 2 | 2.25 |
| 3 | 2.3074 |
| 4 | 2.4414 |
| 5 | 2.4888 |
| 10 | 2.5936 |
| 20 | 2.6534 |
| 50 | 2.6915 |
| 100 | 2.7051 |
| 200 | 2.7164 |

As you see, the higher the value of $n$, the higher the value of the expression $(1+1/n)^n$. Nevertheless, the value of the expression increases more and more slowly as $n$ increases. When $n$ doubles from 1 to 2, the expression increases in value by 0.25. When $n$ doubles from 100 to 200, the expression increases in value only by 0.0113.

The successive values of the expression form a "converging series" which reaches a definite limiting value. That is, the higher the value of $n$, the closer the value of the expression comes to a particular limiting value without ever quite reaching it (let alone getting past it).

The limiting value of the expression $(1+1/n)^n$ as $n$ grows larger without limit, turns out to be an unending decimal, which is conventionally represented by the symbol $e$.

It so happens that the quantity $e$ is extremely important to mathematicians and they have made use of computers to calculate its value to thousands of decimal

103

places. Shall we make do with 50? All right. The value of $e$ is: 2.71828182845904523536028747135266249775724709369995 ...

You may wonder how mathematicians compute the limit of the expression to so many decimal places. Even when I carried $n$ up to 200 and solved for $(1+\frac{1}{200})^{200}$, I only got $e$ correct to two decimal places. Nor can I reach higher values of $n$. I solved the equation for $n=200$ by the use of five-place logarithm tables—the best available in my library—and those aren't accurate enough to handle values of $n$ over 200 in this case. In fact, I don't trust my value for $n=200$.

Fortunately, there are others ways of determining $e$. Consider the following series: $2+\frac{1}{2}+\frac{1}{2}+\frac{1}{6}+\frac{1}{24}+\frac{1}{120}+\frac{1}{720}$ ...

There are six members in this series of numbers as far as I've given it above, and the successive sums are:

| | |
|---|---|
| $2=$ | 2 |
| $2+\frac{1}{2}=$ | 2.5 |
| $2+\frac{1}{2}+\frac{1}{6}=$ | 2.6666 ... |
| $2+\frac{1}{2}+\frac{1}{6}+\frac{1}{24}=$ | 2.7083333 ... |
| $2+\frac{1}{2}+\frac{1}{6}+\frac{1}{24}+\frac{1}{120}=$ | 2.7166666 ... |
| $2+\frac{1}{2}+\frac{1}{6}+\frac{1}{24}+\frac{1}{120}+\frac{1}{720}=$ | 2.71805555 ... |

In other words, by a simple addition of six numbers, a process for which I don't need a table of logarithms at all, I worked out $e$ correct to three decimal places.

If I add a seventh number in the series, then an eighth, and so on, I could obtain $e$ correct to a surprising number of additional decimal places. Indeed, the computer which obtained the value of $e$ to thousands of places made use of the series above, summing thousands of fractions in the series.

But how does one tell what the next fraction in the series will be? In a useful mathematical series, there should be some way of predicting every member of the series from the first few. If I began a series as follows:

$\frac{1}{2}+\frac{1}{3}+\frac{1}{4}+\frac{1}{5}$ . . . you would, without trouble, continue onward . . . $\frac{1}{6}+\frac{1}{7}+\frac{1}{8}$ . . . Similarly, if a series began $\frac{1}{2}+\frac{1}{4}+\frac{1}{8}+\frac{1}{16}$, you would be confident in continuing . . . $\frac{1}{32}+\frac{1}{64}+\frac{1}{128}$ . . .

In fact, an interesting parlor game for number-minded individuals would be to start a series and then ask for the next number. As simple examples consider:

2, 3, 5, 7, 11 . . .

2, 8, 18, 32, 50 . . .

Since the first series is the list of primes, the next number is obviously 13. Since the second series consists of numbers that are twice the list of successive squares, the next number is 72.

But what are we going to do with a series such as:

$2+\frac{1}{2}+\frac{1}{6}+\frac{1}{24}+\frac{1}{120}+\frac{1}{720}$ . . . What is the next number?

If you know, the answer is obvious, but if you *hadn't* known, would you have been able to see it? And if you *don't* know, can you see it?

Just briefly, I am going to introduce a drastic change of subject.

Did any of you ever read Dorothy Sayers' *Nine Tailors*? I did, many years ago. It is a murder mystery, but I remember nothing of the murder, of the characters, of the action, of anything at all but for one item. That one item involves "ringing the changes."

Apparently (I slowly gathered as I read the book) in ringing the changes, you begin with a series of bells tuned to ring different notes, with one man at the rope of each bell. The bells are pulled in order: do, re, mi, fa, and so on. Then, they are pulled again, in a different order. Then, they are pulled again in a still different order. Then, they are pulled again—

You keep it up until all the possible orders (or "changes") in which the bells may be rung *are* rung. One must follow certain rules in doing so, such that no one bell, for instance, can be shifted more than one unit out of its place in the previous change. There are different patterns of shifting the order in the various kinds of change-ringing and these patterns are interesting in themselves. However, all I am dealing with here are the total number of possible changes connected with a fixed number of bells.

Let's symbolize a bell by an exclamation point (!) to represent its clapper, so that we can speak of one bell as 1!, two bells as 2! and so on.

No bells at all can be rung in one way only—by not ringing —so o!=1. One bell (assuming bells *must* be rung if they exist at all) can only be rung in one way— bong—so 1!=1. Two bells, *a* and *b*, can clearly be rung in two ways, *ab* and *ba*, so 2!=2.

Three bells, *a*, *b*, and *c*, can be rung in six ways: *abc*, *acb*, *bac*, *bca*, *cab*, and *cba*, and no more, so 3!=6. Four bells, *a*, *b*, *c*, and *d*, can be rung in just twenty-four different ways. I won't list them all, but you can start with *abcd*, *abdc*, *acbd*, and *acdb* and see how many more changes you can list. If you can list twenty-five different and distinct orders of writing four letters, you have shaken the very foundations of mathematics, but I don't expect you will be able to do it. Anyway, 4!=24.

Similarly (take my word for it for just a moment), five bells can be rung in 120 different changes and six bells in 720, so that 5!=120 and 6!=720.

By now I think you've caught on. Suppose we look again at the series that gives us our value of *e*: $2+\frac{1}{2}+\frac{1}{8}+\frac{1}{24}+\frac{1}{120}+\frac{1}{720}$ ... and write it this way:

$$e=\frac{1}{0!}+\frac{1}{1!}+\frac{1}{2!}+\frac{1}{3!}+\frac{1}{4!}+\frac{1}{5!}+\frac{1}{6!} \ldots$$

Now we know how to generate the fractions next in line. They are ... $+\frac{1}{7!}+\frac{1}{8!}+\frac{1}{9!}$ and so on forever.

To find the values of fractions such as $\frac{1}{7!}$, $\frac{1}{8!}$ and $\frac{1}{9!}$, you must know the value of 7!, 8!, and 9! and to know that you must figure out the number of changes in a set of seven bells, eight bells, and nine bells.

Of course, if you're going to try to list all possible

changes and count them, you'll be at it all day; and you'll get hot and confused besides.

Let's search for a more indirect method, therefore.

We'll begin with four bells, because fewer bells offer no problem. Which bell shall we ring first? Any of the four, of course, so we have four choices for first place. For each one of these four choices, we can choose any of three bells (any one, that is, except the one already chosen for first place) so that for the first two places in line we have $4 \times 3$ possibilities. For each of these we can choose either of the two remaining bells for third place, so that for the first three places, we have $4 \times 3 \times 2$ possibilities. For each of these possibilities there remains only one bell for fourth place, so for all four places there are $4 \times 3 \times 2 \times 1$ arrangements.

We can say then, that $4! = 4 \times 3 \times 2 \times 1 = 24$.

If we work out the changes for any number of bells, we will reach similar conclusions. For seven bells, for instance, the total number of changes is $7 \times 6 \times 5 \times 4 \times 3 \times 2 \times 1 = 5,040$. We can say, then, that $7! = 5,040$.

(The common number of bells used in ringing the changes is seven; a set termed a "peal." If all seven bells are rung through once in six seconds, then a complete set of changes—5,040 of them—requires eight hours, twenty-four minutes . . . And ideally, it should be done without a mistake. Ringing the changes is a serious thing.)

Actually, the symbol "!" does not really mean "bell" (That was just an ingenious device of mine to introduce the matter.) In this case it stands for the word "factorial." Thus, 4! is "factorial four" and 7! is "factorial seven."

Such numbers represent not only the changes that can be rung in a set of bells, but the number of orders in which the cards can be found in a shuffled deck, the number of orders in which men can be seated at a table, and so on.

I have never seen any explanation for the term "factorial" but I can make what seems to me a reasonable stab at explaining it. Since the number $5,040 = 7 \times 6 \times 5 \times 4 \times 3 \times 2 \times 1$, it can be evenly divided by each number from 1 to 7 inclusive. In other words, each number from 1 to 7 is a factor of 5,040; why not, therefore, call 5,040 "factorial seven."

And we can make it general. All the integers from 1 to $n$ are factors of $n!$. Why not call $n!$ "factorial $n$" therefore.

We can see, now, why the series used to determine $e$ is such a good one to use.

The values of the factorial numbers increase at a tremendous rate, as is clear from the list in Table 27 of values up to merely 15!

*Table 27—The Factorials*

| 0! | 1 |
|----|---|
| 1! | 1 |
| 2! | 2 |
| 3! | 6 |
| 4! | 24 |
| 5! | 120 |
| 6! | 720 |
| 7! | 5,040 |
| 8! | 40,320 |
| 9! | 362,880 |
| 10! | 3,628,800 |
| 11! | 39,916,800 |
| 12! | 479,001,600 |
| 13! | 6,227,020,800 |
| 14! | 87,178,921,200 |
| 15! | 1,307,674,368,000 |

As the values of the factorials zoom upward, the value of fractions with successive factorials in the denominator must zoom downward. By the time you reach $\frac{1}{6!}$, the value is only $\frac{1}{720}$, and by the time you reach $\frac{1}{15!}$, the value is considerably less than a trillionth.

Each such factorial-denominatored fraction is larger than the remainder of the series all put together. Thus $\frac{1}{15!}$ is larger than $\frac{1}{16!}+\frac{1}{17!}+\frac{1}{18!}$ . . . and so on and so on forever, all put together. And this preponderance of a particular fraction over all later fractions combined increases as one goes along the series.

Therefore suppose we add up all the terms of the series through $\frac{1}{14!}$. The value is short of the truth by $\frac{1}{15!}+\frac{1}{16!}+\frac{1}{17!}+\frac{1}{18!}$ etc, etc. We might, however, say the value is short of the truth by $\frac{1}{15!}$ because the remainder of the series is insignificant in sum compared to $\frac{1}{15!}$. The value of $\frac{1}{15!}$ is less than a trillionth. It is, in other words, less than 0.000000000001, and the value of $e$ you obtain by summing a little over a dozen fractions is correct to eleven decimal places.

Suppose we summed all the series up to $\frac{1}{999!}$ (by computer, of course). If we do that, we are $\frac{1}{1000!}$ short of the true answer. To find out how much that is, we must have some idea of the value of 1000!. We might determine that by calculating $1000\times999\times998$ . . . and so on, but don't try. It will take forever.

Fortunately, there exist formulas for calculating out large factorials (at least approximately) and there are tables which give the logarithms of these large factorials.

Thus, $log$ 1000!=2567.6046442. This means that $1000!=4.024\times10^{2567}$, or (approximately) a 4 followed by 2,567 zeroes. If the series for $e$ is calculated out to $\frac{1}{999!}$, the value will be short of the truth by only $1/(4\times10^{2567})$ and you will have $e$ correct to 2,566 decimal places. (The best value of $e$ I know of was calculated out to no less than 60,000 decimal places.)

Let me digress once again to recall a time I had personal use for moderately large factorials. When I was in the Army, I went through a period where three fellow sufferers and myself played bridge day and night until one of the others broke up the thing by throwing

109

down his hand and saying, "We've played so many games, the same hands are beginning to show up."

I was terribly thankful, for that gave me something to think about.

Each order of the cards in a bridge deck means a possible different set of bridge hands. Since there are fifty-two cards, the total number of arrangements is 52! However, within any individual hand, the arrangement doesn't matter. A particular set of thirteen cards received by a particular player is the same hand whatever its arrangement. The total number of arrangements of the thirteen cards of a hand is 13! and this is true for each of four hands. Therefore the total number of bridge-hand combinations is equal to the total number of arrangements divided by the number of those arrangements that don't matter, or:

$$\frac{52!}{(13!)^4}$$

I had no tables handy, so I worked it out the long way but that didn't bother me. It took up my time and, for my particular tastes, was much better than a game of bridge. I have lost the original figures long since, but now I can repeat the work with the help of tables.

The value of 52! is, approximately, $8.066 \times 10^{67}$. The value of 13! (as you can see in the table of factorials I gave above) is approximately $6.227 \times 10^9$ and the fourth power of that value is about $1.5 \times 10^{39}$. If we divide $8.066 \times 10^{67}$ by $1.5 \times 10^{39}$, we find that the total number of different bridge games possible is roughly $5.4 \times 10^{28}$ or 54,000,000,000,000,000,000,000,000,000,000 or 54 octillion.

I announced this to my friends. I said, "The chances are not likely that we are repeating games. We could play a trillion games a second for a billion years, without repeating a single game."

My reward was complete incredulity. The friend who had originally complained said, gently, "But, pal, there are only fifty-two cards, you know," and he led me to a quiet corner of the barracks and told me to sit and rest awhile.

Actually, the series used to determine the value of $e$ is only a special example of a general case. It is possible to show that:

$$e^x = x^0/o! + x^1/1! + x^2/2! + x^3/3! + x^4/4! + x^5/5! \ldots$$

Since $x^0 = 1$, for any value of $x$, and o! and 1! both equal 1, the series is usually said to start: $e^x = 1 + x + x^2/2! + x^3/3! \ldots$ but I prefer my version given above. It is more symmetrical and beautiful.

Now $e$ itself can be expressed as $e^1$. In this case, the $x$ of the general series becomes 1. Since 1 to any power equals 1, then $x^2$, $x^3$ $x^4$ and all the rest become 1 and the series becomes:

$$e^1 = \tfrac{1}{0!} + \tfrac{1}{1!} + \tfrac{1}{2!} + \tfrac{1}{3!} + \tfrac{1}{4!} + \tfrac{1}{5!} \ldots$$ which is just the series we've been working with earlier.

But now let's take up the reciprocal of $e$; or, in other words, $1/e$. Its value to fifteen decimal places is 0.367879441171442...

It so happens that $1/e$ can be written as $e^{-1}$, which means that in the general formula for $e^x$, we can substitute $-1$ for $x$.

When $-1$ is raised to a power, the answer is $+1$ if the power is an even one, and $-1$ if it is an odd one. In other words: $(-1)^0 = 1$, $(-1)^1 = -1$, $(-1)^2 = +1$, $(-1)^3 = -1$, $(-1)^4 = +1$, and so on forever.

If, in the general series, then, $x$ is set equal to $-1$, we have:

$$e^{-1} = (-1)^0/0! + (-1)^1/1! + (-1)^2/2! + (-1)^3/3! + (-1)^4/4! \ldots$$ or $e^{-1} = 1/0! + (-1)/1! + \tfrac{1}{2} + (-1)/3! + \tfrac{1}{4}! + (-1)/5! \ldots$ or $e^{-1} = \tfrac{1}{0!} - \tfrac{1}{1!} + \tfrac{1}{2!} - \tfrac{1}{3!} + \tfrac{1}{4!} - \tfrac{1}{5!} + \tfrac{1}{6!} - \tfrac{1}{7!} \ldots$

In other words, the series for $1/e$ is just like the series for $e$ except that all the even terms are converted from additions to subtractions.

Furthermore, since $1/0!$ and $\tfrac{1}{1!}$ both equal 1, the first two terms in the series for $1/e - 1/0! - \tfrac{1}{1!}$ —are

111

equal to $1-1=0$. They may therefore be omitted and we may conclude that:

$$e^{-1} = \tfrac{1}{2!} - \tfrac{1}{3!} + \tfrac{1}{4!} - \tfrac{1}{5!} + \tfrac{1}{6!} - \tfrac{1}{7!} + \tfrac{1}{8!} - \tfrac{1}{9!} + \tfrac{1}{10!},$$ and so on forever.

And now, at last, we come to my own personal discovery! As I looked at the series just given above for $e^{-1}$, I couldn't help think that the alternation between plus and minus is a flaw in its beauty. Could there not be any way in which it could be expressed with pluses only or with minuses only?

Since an expression such as $-\tfrac{1}{3!} + \tfrac{1}{4!}$ can be converted into $-(\tfrac{1}{3!} - \tfrac{1}{4!})$, it seemed to me I could write the following series:

$$e^{-1} = \tfrac{1}{2!} - (\tfrac{1}{3!} - \tfrac{1}{4!}) - (\tfrac{1}{5!} - \tfrac{1}{6!}) - (\tfrac{1}{7!} - \tfrac{1}{8!}) \ldots$$ and so on.

Now we have only minus signs, but we also have parentheses, which again offer an esthetic flaw.

So I considered the contents of the parentheses. The first one contains $\tfrac{1}{3!} - \tfrac{1}{4!}$ which equals $1/(3\times2\times1) - 1/(4\times3\times3\times1)$. This is equal to $(4-1)/(4\times3\times2\times1)$, or to $\tfrac{3}{4!}$. In the same way, $\tfrac{1}{5!} - \tfrac{1}{6!} = \tfrac{5}{6!}$; $\tfrac{1}{7!} - \tfrac{1}{8!} = \tfrac{7}{8!}$ and so on.

I was astonished and inexpressibly delighted for now I had the Asimov Series which goes:

$$e^{-1} = \tfrac{1}{2!} - \tfrac{3}{4!} - \tfrac{5}{6!} - \tfrac{7}{8!} - \tfrac{9}{10!} \ldots$$ and so on forever.

I am certain that this series is at once obvious to any real mathematician and I'm sure it has been described in texts for three hundred years—but I've never seen it and until someone stops me, I'm calling it the Asimov Series.

Not only does the Asimov Series contain only minus signs (except for the unexpressed positive sign before the first term), but it contains all the digits in order. You simply can't ask for anything more beautiful than that. Let's conclude now, by working out just a few terms of the series:

$$\tfrac{1}{2}_1 \qquad\qquad\qquad = 0.5$$
$$\tfrac{1}{2}_1 - \tfrac{3}{4}_1 \qquad\qquad = 0.375$$
$$\tfrac{1}{2}_1 - \tfrac{3}{4}_1 - \tfrac{5}{6}_1 \qquad = 0.3680555\ldots$$
$$\tfrac{1}{2}_1 - \tfrac{3}{4}_1 - \tfrac{5}{6}_1 - \tfrac{7}{8}_1 = 0.3678819\ldots$$

As you see, by adding up only four terms of the series. I get an answer which is only 0.0000025 greater than the truth, an error of 1 part in a bit less than 150,000 or, roughly, $\tfrac{1}{1500}$ of 1 percent.

So if you think the "Exclamation Point" of the title refers only to the factorial symbol, you are wrong. It applies even more so to my pleasure and astonishment with the Asimov Series.

P.S. To get round the unexpressed positive sign in the Asimov Series some readers (after the first appearance in print of this chapter) suggested the series be written: $-(-1)/0_1 - \tfrac{1}{2}_1 - \tfrac{3}{4}_1 \ldots$ All the terms would then indeed be negative, even the first, but we would have to step outside the realm of the natural numbers to include 0 and $-1$, which detracts a bit from the austere beauty of the series.

Another suggested alternative is: $\tfrac{0}{1}_1 + \tfrac{2}{3}_1 + \tfrac{4}{5}_1 + \tfrac{6}{7}_1 + \tfrac{8}{9}_1$ ... which also gives $1/e$. It includes only positive signs which are prettier (in my opinion) than negative signs but, on the other hand, it includes 0.

Still another reader suggested a similar series for $e$ itself; one that goes as follows: $\tfrac{2}{1}_1 + \tfrac{4}{3}_1 + \tfrac{6}{5}_1 + \tfrac{8}{7}_1 + \tfrac{10}{9}_1$ ... The inversion of the order of the natural numbers detracts from its orderliness but it gives it a certain touch of charming grace, doesn't it?

Oh, if only mathematics loved me as I love her!

# 8. DEATH IN THE LABORATORY

I'M A GREAT ONE for iconoclasm. Given half a chance, I love to say something shattering about some revered institution, and wax sarcastically cynical about Mother's Day or apple pie or baseball. Naturally, though, I draw the line at having people say nasty things about institutions I personally revere.

Like Science and Scientists, for instance. (Capital S, you'll notice.)

Scientists have their faults, of course. They can be stodgy and authoritarian and theories can get fixed in place and resist dislodging. There is, for instance, the sad case of the French chemist Auguste Laurent and the Swedish chemist Jöns Jakob Berzelius.

In 1836, Laurent advanced theories concerning the structure of organic compounds that were on the right track, while Berzelius had long maintained views in this respect that had important elements of wrongness. Unfortunately, Laurent was young and little known and Berzelius was the Great Man of chemistry in his time, so Laurent was hounded into obscurity. He was forced to work in third-class poorly heated laboratories, since no important institution would hire him in the face of Berzelius' displeasure, and the poor working conditions aggravated his tubercular condition and brought him to a premature death. Berzelius, on the other hand, died at the peak of his fame and it was only after his death that Laurent's views began to win out.

These things happen, alas, but not as often in science (I like to think) as in any other form of human endeavor.

At any rate, if someone is going to berate Science as an organization in which Authority stifles Initiative, and in which Vain Old Men squash Eager Young Geniuses, and where the lack of the union card of the Ph.D. condemns brilliant amateurs to the outer darkness—it would be nice if some legitimate examples were used.

Occasionally someone treats the discovery of xenon fluoride as an example of the manner in which stodgy theories actually inhibit experimentation.

I can hear them say it: "Stupid lazy chemists just got the idea into their heads that the noble gases formed no compounds so no one bothered to try to see if they *could* form compounds. After all, if everyone *knows* that something can't be done, why try to do it? And yet, if, at any time, any chemist had simply bothered to mix xenon and fluorine in a nickel container—"

It does sound very stupid of a chemist not to stumble on something that easy, doesn't it? Just mix a little xenon and fluorine in a nickel container, and astonish the world, and maybe win a Nobel Prize.

But do you know what would have happened if the average chemist in the average laboratory had tried to mix a little xenon (very rare and quite expensive, by the way) with a little fluorine? A bad case of poisoning, very likely, and quite possibly, death.

If you think I'm exaggerating, let's consider the history of fluorine. That history does not begin with fluorine itself—a pale yellow-green assassin never seen by human eyes until eighty years ago—but with an odd mineral used by German miners about five hundred years ago.

The substance is mentioned by the first great mineralogist of modern times, George Agricola. In 1529, he described its use by German miners. The mineral melted easily (for a mineral) and when added to ore being smelted, the entire mixture melted more easily, thus bringing about a valuable saving of fuel and time.

Something which is liquid flows, and the Latin word for "to flow" is *fluere,* from which we get "fluid" (for any substance that is a liquid or gas and flows) and "fluent" (to describe an easy flow of words). From the same root comes the word Agricola used for the mineral that liquefied and flowed so easily. That word was *fluores.*

In later years, it came to be called "fluorspar," since "spar" is an old miners' term for "rock." Then, when it became customary to add the suffix "-ite" to the names of minerals, a new alternate name was "fluorite." (The name had an important descendant when it was discovered that fluorite, upon exposure to light of one wavelength, gave off light of a longer wavelength. That process came to be known as "fluorescence.")

Fluorite is still used today as a flux (or liquefier) in the making of steel. The centuries pass but a useful property remains a useful property.

In 1670, a German glass-cutter, Heinrich Schwanhard, was working with fluorite and exposing it, for some reason, to the action of strong acids. A vapor was given off and Schwanhard bent close to watch. His spectacles clouded and, presumably, he may have thought the vapor had condensed upon them.

The cloud did not disappear, however, and on closer examination, the spectacles proved to have been etched. The glass had actually been partly dissolved and its smooth surface roughened.

This was very unusual, for few chemicals attack glass, which is one of the reasons chemists use glassware for their equipment. Schwanhard saw a Good Thing in this. He learned to cover portions of glass objects with wax (which protected those portions against the vapors) and etched the rest of the glass. In this way, he formed all sorts of delicate figures in clear glass against a cloudy background. He got himself patronized by the Emperor and did very well, indeed.

But he kept his process secret and it wasn't until 1725 that chemists, generally, learned of this interesting vapor.

Through the eighteenth century, there were occasional reports on fluorite. A German chemist, Andreas Sigismund Marggraf, showed, in 1768, that fluorite did not contain sulfur. He also found that fluorite, treated with acid, produced a vapor that chewed actual holes in his glassware.

However, it was a Swedish chemist, Carl Wilhelm Scheele, who really put the glass-chewing gas on the map about 1780. He, too, acidified fluorite and etched glass. He studied the vapors more thoroughly than any predecessor and maintained the gas to be an acid. Because of this, Scheele is commonly given the credit for having discovered this "fluoric acid" (as it was termed for about a quarter of a century).

The discovery, unfortunately, did Scheele's health no good. He isolated a large number of substances and it was his habit to smell and taste all the new chemicals he obtained, in order that this might serve as part of the routine characterization. Since in addition to the dangerous "fluoride acid," he also isolated such nasty items as hydrogen sulfide (the highly poisonous rotten-egg gas we commonly associate with school chemistry laboratories) and hydrogen cyanide (used in gas-chamber executions), the wonder is that he didn't die with the stuff in his mouth.

His survival wasn't total, though, for he died at the early age of forty-four, after some years of invalidship. There is no question in my mind but that his habit of sniffing and sipping unknown chemicals drastically shortened his life.

117

While most chemists are very careful about tasting, by the way, much more careful than poor Scheele ever was, this cannot be said about smelling, even today. Chemists may not deliberately go about sniffing at things, but the air in laboratories is usually loaded with gases and vapors and chemists often take a kind of perverse pleasure in tolerating this, and in reacting with a kind of superior professional amusement at the non-chemists who make alarmed faces and say "phew."

This may account for the alleged shortened life expectancy of chemists generally. I am not speaking of this shortened life expectancy as an established fact, please note, since I don't know that it is. I say "alleged." Still, there was a letter recently in a chemical journal by someone who had been following obituaries and who claimed that chemists died at a considerably younger age, on the average, than did scientists who were not chemists. This could be so.

There were also speculations some years back that a number of chemists showed mental aberrations in later years through the insidious long-term effects of mercury poisoning. This came about through the constant presence of mercury vapor in the laboratory, vapor that ascended from disregarded mercury droplets in cracks and corners. (All chemists spill mercury now and then.)

To avoid creating alarm and despondency, however, I might mention that some chemists lived long and active lives.* The prize specimen is the French chemist Michel Eugène Chevreul, who was born in 1786 and died in 1889 at the glorious age of one hundred and three! What's more, he was active into advanced old age, for in his nineties he was making useful studies on gerontology (the study of the effect of old age on living organisms) using himself (who else) as a subject. He attended the elaborate celebration of the cen-

*And to those Loyal Readers who may be concerned about my personal welfare, I must admit that for many years now I have entered chemistry laboratories only at rare intervals.

tennial of his own birth and was exuberantly hailed as the "Nestor of science." Indeed, I know of no other scientist of the first class who passed the age of one hundred. If a Gentle Reader knows of one, please let me have the information.

Of course, Chevreul worked with such non-dangerous substances as waxes, soaps, fats, and so on, but consider then the German chemist Robert Wilhelm Bunsen. As a young man he worked with organic compounds of arsenic and poisoned himself nearly to the point of death. At the age of twenty-five, one of those compounds exploded and caused him to lose the sight of one eye. He survived, however, and went on to attain the respectable age of eighty-eight.

Yet it remains a fact that many of the chemists, in the century after Scheele, who did major work on "fluoric acid" died comparatively young.


Once Scheele had established the gas produced from acidified fluorite to be an acid, a misconception at once arose as to its structure. The great French chemist Antoine-Laurent Lavoisier had decided at just about that time that all acids contained oxygen and, indeed, the word "oxygen" is from the Greek phrase meaning "acid producer."

It is true that many acids contain oxygen (sulfuric acid and nitric acid are examples) but some do not. Consider, for instance, a compound called "muriatic acid," from a Latin word meaning "brine" because the acid could be obtained by treating brine with sulfuric acid.

It was supposed, following Lavoisier's dictum, that muriatic acid contained oxygen, was perhaps a compound of oxygen with an as-yet-unknown element called "murium." Scheele found that on treating muriatic acid with certain oxygen-containing compounds, a greenish gas was obtained. He assumed that muriatic acid had added on additional oxygen and named the gas "oxy-muriatic acid."

The English chemist Humphry Davy, however, after careful work with muriatic acid, was able to show that the acid did not contain oxygen. Rather it contained hydrogen and was probably a compound of hydrogen and an as-yet-unknown element. Furthermore, if oxygen combined with muriatic acid, the chances were that it combined with the hydrogen, pulling it away and leaving the as-yet-unknown element in isolation. The greenish gas which Scheele had called oxymuriatic acid was, Davy decided, that element, and in 1810 he renamed it "chlorine" from the Greek word for "green" because of its color.

Since muriatic acid is a compound of hydrogen and chlorine, it came to be known as "hydrogen chloride" (in gaseous form) or "hydrochloric acid" (in water solution).

Other acids were also found to be free of oxygen. Hydrogen sulfide and hydrogen cyanide are examples. (They are very weak acids, to be sure, but the oxygen-in-acid proponents could not fall back on the assumption that oxygen is required for *strong* acids, since hydrochloric acid, though not containing oxygen, is, nevertheless, a strong acid.)

Davy went on to show that fluoric acid was another example of an acid without oxygen. Furthermore, fluoric acid had certain properties that were quite reminiscent of hydrogen chloride. It occurred to a French physicist, André Marie Ampère, therefore, that fluoric acid might well be a compound of hydrogen with an element very like chlorine. He said as much to Davy, who agreed.

By 1813, Ampère and Davy were giving the new element (not yet isolated or studied) the same suffix as that possessed by chlorine in order to emphasize the similarity. The stem of the name would come from fluorite, of course, and the new element was "fluorine," a name that has been accepted ever since. Fluoric acid became "hydrogen fluoride" and fluorite became "calcium fluoride."

The problem now arose of isolating fluorine so that it might be studied. This proved to be a problem of the first magnitude. Chlorine could be isolated from hydrochloric acid by having oxygen, so to speak, snatch the hydrogen from chlorine's grip, leaving the latter isolated as the element. Oxygen was more active than chlorine, you see, and pulled more strongly at hydrogen than chlorine could.

The same procedure could not, however, be applied to hydrogen fluoride. Oxygen could not, under any conditions, snatch hydrogen from the grip of fluorine. (It was found, many years later, that elementary fluorine could, instead, snatch hydrogen from oxygen. Fluorine, in reacting with water—a compound of hydrogen and oxygen—snatches at the hydrogen with such force that the oxygen is liberated in the unusually energetic form of ozone.)

The conclusion was inescapable that fluorine was more active than chlorine and oxygen. In fact, there seemed reason to suspect that fluorine might be the most active element in existence (a deduction that later chemists amply confirmed) and that no simple chemical reaction could liberate fluorine from compounds such as hydrogen fluoride or calcium fluoride, since no other element could force hydrogen or calcium out of the strong grip of fluorine.

But then, who says it is necessary to restrict one's self to chemical reactions? In 1800, the electric battery was invented and within weeks, it had been found that an electric current passing through a compound could split it apart ("electrolysis") where ordinary chemical reactions might be able to perform that task only under extreme conditions. Water, for instance, was broken up to hydrogen and oxygen. Hydrogen (and various metals) can be made to appear at the negative electrode, while oxygen (and other non-metals) can be made to appear at the positive electrode.

Davy applied this technique to various compounds which chemists were sure contained still-unknown metals that were so active that ordinary chemical techniques did not suffice to break them loose. In 1807 and 1808, making use of the most powerful electric battery that had yet been constructed, he quickly isolated six extremely active metals: potassium, sodium, calcium, magnesium, strontium, and barium. All appeared at the negative electrode, of course.

There was no reason, it seemed to Davy, that the same technique might not work with calcium fluoride. Here the calcium would appear at the negative electrode and fluorine at the positive. He tried it and got nowhere. Oh, he might have isolated fluorine at the positive electrode, but as soon as it was formed, it attacked whatever was in sight: water, glass, even silver or platinum, which Davy had used as his container. In no time at all, Davy had fluorine compounds on his hands, but no fluorine.

It was a losing proposition in another way, too, for Davy managed to be severely poisoned during his work on fluorine compounds, through breathing small quantities of hydrogen fluoride. It didn't kill him, but it undoubtedly contributed to the fact that he died at the age of fifty after some years of invalidism.

Others were less lucky than Davy, even. In the 1830s, two English brothers, Thomas and George Knox, decided not to take it for granted that fluorine could not be liberated by chemical means (scientists are not as stodgy as their critics like to pretend). They tried to coax chlorine into reacting with mercury fluoride, accepting the mercury and liberating the fluorine. They failed, and both underwent long and agonizing sieges of hydrogen fluoride poisoning.

A Belgian chemist, P. Louyet, who had followed the

attempts of the Knox brothers closely, tried to repeat their work and failed even more spectacularly. He was killed entirely by hydrogen fluoride.

One of Louyet's assistants was the French chemist Edmond Frémy. He had watched some of Louyet's experiments and decided that trying to isolate fluorine by chemical reactions got one nothing but a ticket to the morgue. He returned to Davy's electrolytic method and worked with the most gingerly caution. His reward was that he lived to be eighty.

In 1885, he repeated Davy's attempt to electrolyze calcium fluoride with the same results—any fluorine that developed tackled everything in reach and was gone at once.

He next decided to work with hydrogen fluoride itself. Hydrogen fluoride is a liquid at slightly less than room temperatures and can be more easily dealt with. It needn't be kept red-hot during the electrolysis as calcium fluoride has to be.

Unfortunately, hydrogen fluoride in Frémy's day was always obtained in water solution. To try to electrolyze a water solution of hydrogen fluoride meant that two different elements could come off at the positive electrode, oxygen or fluorine. Since oxygen was less active and more easily pulled away from hydrogen, only oxygen appeared at the electrode if there was even a small quantity of water present in the hydrogen fluoride.

Frémy therefore worked out methods for producing completely water-free hydrogen fluoride: "anhydrous hydrogen fluoride." He was the first to do so. Unfortunately, he found himself stymied. Anhydrous hydrogen fluoride would not pass an electric current. If he added some water, an electric current would pass—but only oxygen would be produced.

In the end, he, too, gave up and as the 1880s dawned, fluorine was still victor. It had defeated the best efforts of many first-class chemists for three-quarters of a century; had invalided some and killed others outright.

Frémy had a student, the French chemist Ferdinand Frédéric Henri Moissan, who took up the battle, and proceeded to attack the fluorine problem with bulldog tenacity.

He went back to chemical methods once again. He decided he must begin with a fluorine compound that was relatively unstable. The more stable a compound after all, the more tightly fluorine is holding the other atoms and the more difficult it is to pry that fluorine loose.

In 1884, Moissan came to the conclusion that phosphorus fluoride was comparatively unstable (for a fluoride). This seemed particularly hopeful since phosphorus happened to be unusually avid in its tendency to combine with oxygen. Perhaps in this case, oxygen could pull atoms away from fluorine. Moissan tried and succeeded only partially. The oxygen grabbed at the phosphorus all right but the fluorine did not let go and Moissan ended with a compound in which phosphorus was combined with both oxygen and fluorine.

Moissan tried another tack. Platinum is an extremely inert metal; even fluorine attacks it only with difficulty. Hot platinum, however, does seem to have the ability to combine easily with phosphorus. If he passed phosphorus fluoride over hot platinum, would the platinum perhaps combine with phosphorus rather than with fluorine, and set the fluorine free?

No such luck. Both phosphorus and fluorine combined with the platinum and in a matter of minutes a lot of expensive platinum was ruined for nothing. (Fortunately for Moissan, he had a rich father-in-law, who subsidized him generously.)

Moissan, like Frémy before him, decided to back away from straight chemistry and try electrolysis.

He began with arsenic fluoride and after fiddling with that, unsuccessfully, he decided to abandon that line of investigation because he was beginning to suffer from arsenic poisoning. So he turned to hydrogen fluoride (and underwent four different episodes of hydrogen fluoride poisoning, which eventually helped bring him to his death at the age of fifty-four).

Moissan remembered perfectly well that Frémy's anhydrous hydrogen fluoride would not carry an electric current. Something had to be added to make it do so, but not something that would offer an alternate element for production at the positive electrode. Why not another fluoride? Moissan dissolved potassium hydrogen fluoride in the anhydrous hydrogen fluoride and had a mixture which could pass a current and which could produce only fluorine at the positive electrode.

Furthermore, he made use of equipment built up out of an alloy of platinum and iridium, an alloy that was even more resistant to fluorine than platinum itself was.

Finally, he brought his entire apparatus to −50°C. All chemical reactions are slowed as temperature decreases and at −50°C even fluorine's savagery ought to be subdued.

Moissan turned on the current and hydrogen bubbled off the negative electrode like fury, but nothing showed at the positive electrode. He stopped to think. The positive electrode was inserted into the platinum-iridium vessel through a stopper. The stopper had to be an insulator so it couldn't be platinum or any metal; and that stopper had been eaten up by flourine. No wonder he hadn't gotten any gas.

Moissan needed a stopper made of something that would not carry an electric current and would be untouched by fluorine. It occurred to him that the mineral fluorite already had all the fluorine it could carry and would not be attacked further. He therefore carefully carved stoppers out of fluorite and repeated the experiment.

On June 26, 1886, he obtained a pale yellow-green gas about his positive electrode. Fluorine had finally been isolated, and when Moissan later repeated the experiment in public, his old teacher Frémy watched.

Moissan went on, in 1899, to discover a less expensive way of producing fluorine. He made use of copper vessels. Fluorine attacked copper violently, but after the copper was overlaid with copper fluoride, no further attacks were to be expected. In 1906, the year before his death, Moissan received the Nobel Prize in chemistry for his feat.

Even so, fluorine remained the bad boy of the table of elements for another generation. It could be isolated and used; but not easily and not often. Most of all, it couldn't be handled with anything but supreme caution for it was even more poisonous than hydrogen fluoride.

Meanwhile the noble gases were discovered in the 1890s and although they were recognized as being extremely inert, chemists tried over and over to force them into some kind of compound formation. (Don't believe the myth that chemists were so sure that the noble gases wouldn't react that they never tried to test the fact. Dozens of compounds were reported in the literature—but the reports, until quite recently, always proved to be mistaken.)

It wasn't until the early 1930s that chemical theory had been developed to the point where one need not tackle the noble gases at random in an effort to form compounds. The American chemist Linus Pauling, in 1933, was able to show, through logical arguments, that xenon ought to be able to form compounds with fluorine. Almost at once two chemists at Pauling's school, the California Institute of Technology, took up the challenge. They were Donald M. Yost and Albert L. Kaye.

All the xenon they could get hold of was 100 cc worth at normal air pressure and they could get hold of no fluorine. They had to rig up a device of their own to prepare fluorine; and it worked only intermittently. Doing the best they could, they found they could obtain no clear signs of any compound. Neither were they completely certain that no compound had been formed. The results were inconclusive.

There was no immediate follow-up. The results didn't warrant it. Chemists knew the murderous history of fluorine, and enthusiasm for such experiments ran low.

During World War II, fluorine was needed in connection with atomic bomb research. Under that kind of pressure, methods for the production of fluorine in quantity, and in *reasonable security* were developed.

By the 1950s, it was finally possible to run non-military experiments, involving fluorine, without much risk of suicide. Even then, there were only a few laboratories equipped for such work and those had a great many things to do with fluorine other than mixing them with noble gases.

"Just mix xenon and fluoride in a nickel container" indeed. It could not have been done, in reasonable safety and with reasonable hopes of success, any more than ten years before it actually was done in 1962; and, under the circumstances, the ten years' delay was a remarkably reasonable one and reflects no discredit whatever on Science.

# 9. TO TELL A CHEMIST

SOME TIME AGO, I watched a television program called "To Tell the Truth." If you are unaware of its nature, I will explain that it involves a panel of four, who try to guess which one, of three people claiming to be John Smith, is the *real* John Smith. They do so by asking questions which, they hope, the real John Smith (pledged to tell the truth) can answer correctly, while the phonies, however primed, cannot.

The reason I watched was that Catherine de Camp (the lovely and charming wife of L. Sprague de Camp) was scheduled to appear as a contestant in her capacity as archaeologist. To my surprise, two of the four panelists would not believe she was the real Catherine de Camp. Her case seemed shaken when, in answer to one question, she stated that Atlantis had never existed. The stir of disapproval among the panelists was marked. Surely, no real archaeologist (they were plainly thinking) would deny the existence of Atlantis.

And it got me to thinking—

How does one distinguish quickly and easily between a specialist and a well-primed non-specialist? It seems to me you must find little things no one would ever think to prime the non-specialist upon.

Since I know the chemical profession best, I devised two questions, for instance, to tell a chemist from a non-chemist. Here they are:

1) How do you pronounce UNIONIZED?
2) What is a mole?

128

In response to the first question, the non-chemist is bound to say "YOON-yun-ized," which is the logical pronunciation, and the dictionary pronunciation, too. The chemist, however, would never think of such a thing; he would say without a moment's hesitation: "un-EYE-on-ized."

In response to the second question, the non-chemist is bound to say, "A little furry animal that burrows underground," unless he is a civil engineer who will say, "A breakwater." A chemist, on the other hand, will clear his throat, and say, "Well, it's like this—" and keep talking for hours.

There's my cue. Shall we talk about the chemical version of the little furry animal?

To do so, we will begin with molecules. The oxygen molecule, consisting of 2 oxygen atoms, has a molecular weight of 32; while the hydrogen molecule, consisting of 2 hydrogen atoms, has a molecular weight of 2. Such molecular weights are pure numbers and it is not necessary to go into their significance here. All we have to understand at this moment is that the ratio of the mass of an oxygen molecule to that of a hydrogen molecule is indicated by their respective molecular weights to be 32 to 2.

If we take 2 molecules of oxygen and 2 of hydrogen, the mass of each substance is doubled, but the ratio remains the same. The ratio also remains the same if we take 10 of each type of molecule, or 100 of each, or 5,266 of each, and so on.

We can make it general and say that as long as we have equal numbers of molecules of hydrogen and of oxygen, the total mass of the oxygen molecules is to the total mass of the hydrogen molecules as 32 is to 2.

We can begin with a 2-gram sample of hydrogen. This contains a certain number of hydrogen molecules, which we will call $N$. Imagine that we also have a sample of oxygen which contains $N$ oxygen molecules. Since the two gas samples contain equal numbers of molecules, the mass of the oxygen to that of the hydrogen is as 32 is to 2. The mass of the hydrogen has been set at 2 grams, therefore the mass of the oxygen is 32 grams.

We conclude that 2 grams of hydrogen and 32 grams of oxygen both contain $N$ molecules.

Notice the significance of the 2-gram sample of hydrogen. It is the numerical value of the molecular weight (2) expressed in grams. We can therefore refer to 2 grams as the "gram-molecular-weight" of hydrogen. (Similarly, 2 pounds of hydrogen would be the pound-molecular-weight, 2 tons of hydrogen would be the ton-molecular-weight, and so on. We will confine ourselves, however, to gram-molecular-weights.)

By the same reasoning, 32 grams of oxygen is a gram-molecular-weight of oxygen.

Now the phrase "gram-molecular-weight" contains six syllables. Since chemists must use the phrase very frequently, they sought avidly for some shortened version. You will note that the fifth to eighth letters inclusive are "m-o-l-e." With a wild cry of delight, chemists shortened "gram-molecular-weight" to "mole."

Some of them, in the nervous realization that a "mole" is a little, furry animal that burrows underground, try to use "mol" instead. I was forced to use "mol," in a textbook I once wrote, by the overriding vote of my two coauthors, a state of affairs which led to internal bleeding. The word is universally pronounced with a long "o" and "mol" must clearly have a short "o." Consequently, in this chapter, where I am my own master, I use "mole." Do you hear me, world? "Mole!"

Very well, then, I have already shown that 1 mole of hydrogen and 1 mole of oxygen both have the same number ($N$) of molecules. By similar reasoning, it is possible to show that 1 mole of any substance at all contains $N$ molecules.

As examples, the molecular weight of water is 18, that of sulfuric acid is 98, and that of table sugar (sucrose) is 342. There are, therefore, $N$ molecules in 18 grams of water, in 98 grams of sulfuric acid, and in 342 grams of sucrose.

Now I have explained the mole, but one thing leads to another, and I refuse to stop.

For instance, suppose you collect 1 mole of hydrogen (2 grams) and keep it at what is called "standard temperature and pressure" (STP), which means a temperature of 0°C and a pressure of 1 atmosphere. You will find that the hydrogen will take up a volume of 22.4 liters.

Suppose you next do the same for 1 mole of oxygen (32 grams). Its volume at STP is *also* 22.4 liters. In fact, take 22.4 liters of any gas, and though the mass of the gas may vary all over the lot, you will always find yourself with 1 mole.*

In the same way, 11.2 liters of any gas contain 0.5 moles of that gas; 44.8 liters of any gas contain 2 moles of that gas; and so on. In fact, we can make the following statement: "Equal volumes of gases under fixed conditions of temperature and pressure contain equal numbers of molecules."

This statement is easy to work out once there is a grasp of the atomic theory of matter, plus the simple observation that 2 grams of hydrogen and 32 grams of oxygen take up the same volume.

The statement was first made in 1811, however, by an Italian physicist named Amedeo Avogadro, at a time when the atomic theory had just been broached and was barely invading the chemical consciousness. The statement (still called "Avogadro's hypothesis" to this day) seemed, at the time it was made, to be pulled out of

*Actually, this is precisely true only in the case of a "perfect gas," which I will mention again later in the article. Actual gases deviate slightly from this state of affairs, and some gases deviate quite a bit. To make my point here, however, I shall overlook minor imperfections.

thin air and was generally ignored. It took fifty years before its worth and value were appreciated and, as you might expect, Avogadro died just a few years too soon to see himself vindicated.

The next question is, what is the value of $N$? How many molecules are there in 1 mole of any substance? Obviously, it is a very large number since molecules are so small, but that was as far as anyone could go at first. Avogadro, in his lifetime, hadn't the slightest idea of what the exact value of $N$ might be; and neither had anyone else.

It wasn't until 1865 that a German physicist, J. Loschmidt, worked out a reasonable value for the first time, following a particular theoretical approach. Since then, at least a dozen different approaches have been utilized, and all have yielded virtually the same result. The number of molecules in 1 mole of a substance (called "Avogadro's number," by the way) turns out to be, using the value officially accepted in 1963, $6.02252 \times 10^{23}$. If you want that written out in full, it is 602,252,000,000,000,000,000,000; or, in words, it is a little over six hundred sextillion.

From Avogadro's number, you can work out the actual mass of any molecule, by dividing the number into the molecular weight. Thus, since 32 grams of oxygen contains $6,022552 \times 10^{23}$ oxygen molecules, one oxygen molecule has a mass of 32 divided by $6.02252 \times 10^{23}$, or about $5.31 \times 10^{-23}$ grams (0.000000000000000- 0000000531 grams).

It may seem unfair to you that Avogadro's name is attached to a number he never worked out, but it doesn't to me, for he was the one who made the crucial mental leap in this respect. However, if you are one who finds the apparent unfairness rankling, feel relieved! Loschmidt, who first worked out the value of Avogadro's number, is himself appropriately honored. The number of molecules in 1 cubic centimeter of gas at STP is "Loschmidt's number." Since 1 mole of gas takes up 22.4 liters, or to be more precise, 22,415 cubic centimeters, at STP, Loschmidt's number is Avogadro's number divided by 22,415.

Loschmidt's number therefore comes out to be $2.68683 \times 10^{19}$, or 26,868,300,000,000,000,000, or just under twenty-seven quintillion.

Now we can have fun and games with Loschmidt's number (which we will symbolize as $L$).

If there are $L$ molecules in 1 cubic centimeter of gas, then the average distance between the center of one molecule and that of its neighbor is equal to the reciprocal of the cube root of $L$; that is to $1/\sqrt[3]{L}$.

Working this out (I'll do it myself; I needn't plague you with everything), it becomes apparent that the average intermolecular distance in a gas at STP is $3.33 \times 10^{-7}$ centimeters. This is a very short distance for it is about a third of a millionth of a centimeter and a centimeter is about two-fifths of an inch. We might well feel justified in considering gases to be choked to bursting with molecules.

Let's consider matters further, however. A hundred-millionth of a centimeter ($10^{-8}$ centimeters) is an "Angstrom unit," which is usually abbreviated as A. This means that the average intermolecular distance in a gas at STP can be expressed as 33.3 A.

But the radius of a small molecule is in the neighborhood of a little over 3 A. This means that the separation between small molecules is some 10 times the radius of those same molecules. If one of those molecules were expanded to the size of the Earth, its neighbor (also the size of the Earth) would be 40,000 miles away, or something more than one-sixth the distance between the Earth and the Moon. That might be quite close astronomically, but certainly the Earth would not feel particularly crowded with a neighbor at such a distance.

In fact, the amount of space taken up by small gas molecules would be only $\frac{1}{1000}$ of the total volume of the gas. To put it another way, ordinary gases are something like 99.9 percent intermolecular space and only 0.1 percent molecules.

From that standpoint, gases aren't crowded with matter at all. They might, instead, be looked upon as reasonable approaches to vacuum.

Notice that I've been specifying standard temperature and pressure. If the pressure is increased it is easy to push the molecules closer together, considering how much empty space there is in gases. In fact, doubling the pressure halves the volume of the gas, tripling the pressure reduces the volume to one-third, and so on (provided there is no temperature change).

You might wonder why the gas molecules don't fall together of their own accord. Why should they stay so far apart anyway? The answer is that they possess energy which expresses itself in the form of rapid motion, and this motion jostles the molecules apart, so to speak, through incessant collisions. If the pressure is relieved, the molecular jostling moves the molecules correspondingly farther apart. If the pressure is reduced to one-half, the volume of the gas doubles; if the pressure is reduced to one-third, the volume triples, and so on (provided, again, there is no temperature change).

If the temperature is increased (and the pressure is left unchanged), the molecular velocity increases, the jostling is more energetic and the volume increases. If the temperature falls, the volume decreases. There is thus a neat interlocking among the temperature, pressure, and volume of a particular sample of gas. If the gas is perfect, the relationship can be expressed as a very simple "equation of state." For actual gases, the equation has to be modified and made more complicated, but we'll discuss that another time, perhaps.

The first to note the relationship of pressure and volume in gases was the English chemist Robert Boyle, in 1662. In 1677, a French physicist, Edme Mariotte, discovered the relationship independently and was the first to specify that temperature must be kept unchanged. In Great Britain and America, we therefore speak of "Boyle's Law" and in Continental Europe of "Mariotte's Law."

In 1699, a French physicist, Guillaume Amontons, noted the effect of temperature on air, and the manner in which volume and temperature were interrelated. Another French physicist, Jacques A. C. Charles, repeated the observation in 1787 and noted that it applied to all gases and not to air alone. Charles did not publish, however, and a French chemist, Joseph Louis Gay-Lussac, who repeated the observation yet again in 1802, *did* publish. The relationship is therefore referred to as either "Charles's law" or "Gay-Lussac's law." Poor Amontons gets nothing.

So far, the development of understanding concerning the equation of state for gases was the result of purely empirical observation. In the 1860s, however, the Scottish mathematical physicist James Clerk Maxwell accepted a gas as a collection of perfectly elastic molecules engaged in rapid random motion and treated the collection of molecules by means of a rigorous statistical interpretation. An Austrian physicist, Ludwig Boltzmann, did the same independently. Together, they showed that such an interpretation could account for the pressure/temperature/volume relationships beautifully.

Thus was developed the "kinetic theory of gases" ("kinetic" coming from a Greek word for "motion") and it was from this kinetic theory, and the equations it produced, that Loschmidt worked out Avogadro's number for the first time. See how science hangs together!

Maxwell's kinetic theory made use of two assumptions that aren't perfectly correct. To simplify matters, he supposed that the individual gas molecules were of zero size and that there was no mutual molecular attraction. A gas for which these assumptions are correct is the

135

perfect gas I mentioned earlier. In actual gases, the molecules are tiny, but not of zero size, and there is a tiny, but not zero, mutual attraction. Hence, actual gases are more or less imperfect. The imperfection is least in the cases of the gases helium, hydrogen, and neon, where the molecules (or, in the case of helium and neon, single atoms) are smallest and the mutual attraction least.

We can pretend, though, that we are dealing with a perfect gas and consider the effect of temperature. If we begin with a mole of perfect gas at STP, we find the volume is 22,415 cubic centimeters. For every degree C we raise the temperature, the volume increases by a trifle over 82 cubic centimeters, and for every degree C by which we drop the temperature, the volume decreases by a trifle over 82 cubic centimeters.

If we continue dropping the temperature, degree by degree, and if 82 cubic centimeters peels off the volume with each degree, then by the time we reach a temperature of $-273.15°C$, the volume has decreased to zero. It was this fact which first gave rise to the notion of $-273.15°C$ as an "absolute zero," an ultimate cold which could not be surpassed.

Of course, it is only in a perfect gas with molecules of zero size that a shrinkage of volume to zero can be visualized. In any actual gas, with molecules of some definite size, volume can shrink only to the point where the molecules make surface-to-surface contact, at which point the situation changes radically.

Suppose that the molecules of a particular gas have a radius of 1 A. At surface contact, the molecules are separated, center to center, by a distance equal to the sum of their radii; that is, by a distance of 2 A. We can calculate at what temperature this should happen.

At 0°C the center-to-center separation it 33.3 A and at $-273.15°C$ the separation is (ideally) zero. The distance declines smoothly with falling temperature so that we find that at $-257°C$ the separation has decreased to 2 A and surface-to-surface contact has been made. Since —257°C is about 16° above absolute zero, it can be written 16°K (where K stands for Kelvin; Lord Kelvin having been the first to make use of a temperature scale that placed zero at the absolute zero).

If the molecule is particularly small so that the radius is only 0.5 A, surface-to-surface contact would be made at a temperature of 8°K.

Once surface-to-surface contact is made, the substance —under ordinary circumstances at least—is not likely to behave as a gas any further. We have, instead, a "condensed phase."

When surface-to-surface contact is first made, the molecules will still possess sufficient energy to slide around freely. They are then in the "liquid state." If the temperature falls lower and energy is further subtracted, the molecules lock into place and the substance is in the "solid state."

It would seem from what I have said so far that the perfect gas would never liquefy since its molecules would never make surface-to-surface contact, short of absolute zero itself, and absolute zero cannot be reached. Actual gases, however—or so it would seem—must liquefy at temperatures short of absolute zero, but not very far short.

This is more or less true for the three actual gases which, of all gases, are nearest to perfection. Helium, the most nearly perfect, liquefies at 4.2°K, hydrogen at 20.3°K, and neon at 27.2°K. Other gases, however, liquefy at considerably higher temperatures. Oxygen, for instance, which is not terribly imperfect, has a liquefaction point of 90.1°K.

At 90.1°K, the molecules of gas have an average separation, center-to-center, of about 11 A. Even if we allow the oxygen molecule a radius of 2 A, the surface-to-surface separation would be 7 A. The temperature could drop down to close to 30°K before surface-to-surface contact was made.

137

Nevertheless, oxygen liquefies at 90.1°K and not at 30°K. To explain that, we must remember the second imperfection of actual gases; the fact that there is an attraction between molecules. In the mase of helium, hydrogen, and neon, this attraction is very small. If helium atoms happen to collide the mutual attraction is so small it is easily overcome even by the small amount of energy of motion present at extremely low temperatures. For that reason, liquefaction of helium doesn't take place till surface-to-surface contact enforces it.

The mutual attraction among oxygen molecules, however, is considerably higher than among helium or neon atoms or among hydrogen molecules. By the time the temperature has sunk to 90.1°K, the energy of motion is no longer sufficient to pull apart two molecules that have happened to collide. The attraction among oxygen molecules is sufficiently large to hold the combination in place, and oxygen liquefies.

A great many substances possess intermolecular (or interatomic or interionic) attractions so great that they are not gases even at high temperature; a few not until a temperature of 6000°C is reached.

Now let's tackle the condensed phases, beginning with liquid hydrogen. This has a density of 0.07 grams per cubic centimeter at its boiling point (the lowest density, in fact, for the condensed phase of any substance).

Since 2 grams of hydrogen (1 mole) contain $6.02252 \times 10^{23}$ molecules, 0.07 grams contain approximately $2.09 \times 10^{22}$ molecules. The average center-to-center separation of the molecules is, therefore, 3.63 A. This can be taken as the effective diameter of the hydrogen molecule in liquid hydrogen. (For an oxygen molecule, similar calculations yield a diameter of about 3.9 A.)

You might suppose, that as one went up the table of elements to more and more complex atoms, that the atomic diameters, calculated from the density of the condensed phases of the elements, would get steadily larger. This, however, is not so.

The atomic volume is largely determined by the amount of space taken up by the electrons of the atom, and a great deal depends on just how those electrons are arranged. The electrons are arranged in shells and in some atoms, the outermost shell is occupied by a single electron, which is usually held quite weakly and moves far out from the nucleus, giving that atom an unusually large volume.

This is true for sodium, potassium, rubidium, and cesium, for instance, with cesium the most extreme case, for it has more electrons all together than the other atoms of its type.

Cesium, like metals generally, is considered as being made up of single atoms not arranged in molecular combinations. The atomic weight of cesium is 132.9 so that 132.9 grams is the "gram-atomic-weight." (This is not a gram-molecular-weight, so it shouldn't, strictly speaking, be referred to as a "mole.") The gram-atomic-weight of an element contains Avogadro's number of atoms.

The density of cesium at room temperature is 1.87 grams per cubic centimeter so that 1 cubic centimeter of cesium contains about $8.15 \times 10^{21}$ atoms. The effective diameter of of the cesium atom in solid cesium is therefore about 5 A.

On the other hand, when the outermost shell is about half full of electrons, the atom is quite small. The electrons are drawn unusually close to the central nucleus, and this means that neighboring atoms can be drawn unusually close together.

In fact, the compactness of packing proceeds in periodic waves if one plots it against atomic weight. The atomic diameter rises to a peak, and packing is least compact each time a one-electron-in-the-outermost-shell point is reached; and atomic diameter falls to a trough, and packing is most compact each time the outermost-shell-half-full situation is reached. It was this which, in 1870, gave the German chemist Lothar Meyer the notion of the "periodic table" of elements. (Meyer, however, was beaten to the punch by the Russian chemist Dmitri I. Mendeléev, who reached the same conclusion by another line of argument just a few months earlier. But that is another story.)

Examples of regions in the periodic table of particularly small atoms are, in order of increasing complexity of atomic structure: 1) beryllium, boron, and carbon, 2) iron, cobalt, and nickel, 3) ruthenium, rhodium, and palladium, and 4) osmium, iridium, and platinum.

Without going into all the mathematical details, here are some interatomic distances in the room-temperature solid (and, therefore, the effective atomic diameters). Carbon (in the form of diamond) 1.8 A; nickel, 2.2 A; rhodium, 2.4 A; and osmium 2.4 A.

Diamond is the most compact of all solids. This, combined with the fact that each carbon atom in diamond is firmly held by each of four record-close neighbors, is what makes diamond the hardest known substance (with the possible exception of boron nitride, which closely mimics the diamond situation).

The more compact a solid is, the denser it is, and the more massive the individual atoms are, the more extreme the density. Of the various groups of compact atoms, the most massive are those of the three elements, osmium, iridium, and platinum. They should be, therefore, and *are*, the densest of the elements (or, indeed, of any substance).

The density of platinum is 21.37 grams per cubic centimeter, that of iridium is 22.42 grams per cubic centimeter, and that of osmium, the record holder, 22.5 grams per cubic centimeter. Osmium is just about twice as dense as lead, and is ⅙ denser than gold. A cubic foot is not a very large volume, but a cubic foot of osmium weighs 1,400 pounds.

Naturally, the farther apart atoms are (center-to-center) the less trouble it is, all other things being equal, to pull them apart altogether, whether by heat or by the chemical pull of other atoms. Thus, the loosely packed cesium has a melting point of 28.5°C and a boiling point of 670°C, while osmium melts at 2700°C and boils at some temperature higher than 5300°C.

Of all solids, carbon is the most compact, and it also has the highest melting point. It is close to 3700°C before it ceases to be a solid. (Actually it sublimes, rather than melts, turning into gaseous carbon.)

Again, cesium is so ready to leave the society of its fellows and join with other atoms that it is the most active of all metals. Osmium, iridium, and platinum, are, on the other hand, the least active of all metals.

You see?

Beginning students of chemistry often think of the science as a mere collection of disconnected data to be memorized by brute force. Not at all! Just look at it properly and everything hangs together and makes sense.

Of course, getting the hang of the proper look isn't always easy.

# 10. THE CERTAINTY OF UNCERTAINTY

IN HIGH SCHOOL, one of the pieces of literature I was required to read was James Barrie's *The Admirable Crichton*. I reacted to it quite emotionally, but that is not the point at this moment. What is the point is that one of the characters, a well-born young goof named Ernest, had carefully polished up an epigram which he sprang several times during the play.

It went, "After all, I'm not young enough to know everything."

And whenever he said it, someone would answer (impatiently, if the head of the family; wearily, if one of the ladies; paternally, if the competent butler), "You mean you're not *old* enough to know everything."

Ernest nearly died of frustration and so did I, for *I* knew what he meant.*

The memory of the epigram stays with me because, as it happens, nineteenth-century science was young enough to know everything. Near the opening of that century, the French astronomer Pierre Simon de Laplace had said, "If we knew the exact position and velocity of every particle in the universe at any one particular moment, then we could work out all the past and future of the universe."

_____

*He meant that young people *thought* they knew everything, but that as they grew older and wiser they realized they didn't. Good Lord!

The universe, in other words, was completely determinate, and when I read of this (being a convinced determinist myself) I fairly licked my lips with pleasure.

Of course, I understood that we didn't actually know the exact position and velocity of every particle in the universe at any one particular moment, and that we almost certainly never would. However, we could know them *in principle* and that made the universe completely determinate *in principle*.

Wasn't it a great feeling, though, to be young enough to know everything!

But alas we grow older and wiser and knowledge slips through our fingers after all and leaves us naked in a cold and hostile universe. My day of reckoning came in 1936 when I read "Uncertainty," a two-part serial by John W. Campbell, Jr., in *Amazing Stories*. For the first time in my life I found out that the universe was not completely determinate, and couldn't be completely determinate *even in principle*.

So let's talk about uncertainty.

The basic principle is this: The very act of measurement alters the quantity being measured.

The most common example used to illustrate this is the measurement of the temperature of a container of hot water. The easiest way is to insert a thermometer, but if the thermometer is at room temperature, as it probably is, it withdraws heat from the water and when it finally registers a temperature, that temperature is slightly less than the temperature was before the thermometer was inserted.

This difficulty might be circumvented if the thermometer happened to be exactly at the temperature of the water to begin with. But in that case, how would you know the right temperature to begin with unless you measured it first?

Of course, the thermometer might just happen to be at the right temperature, and you could tell that because

143

after insertion into the water the reading would remain the same as before. The thermometer would neither gain nor lose heat; and the temperature of the water would remain as it was and you would have the true and exact temperature.

You wouldn't even have to rely on pure chance. You could, for instance, perform a "thought experiment" (that is one which is conceivable, but which supposes conditions far too ideal and tedious to put into actual practice). We could divide our sample of water into independent sections each at the same temperature as all the rest.

We can then stick thermometers into the various sections, each thermometer being carefully warmed in advance to a different temperature, at one-degree intervals. One of those thermometers will register the same temperature before and after and there you would have the true and exact temperature.

Well, true and exact to the nearest degree anyway. Of course, that is just a detail, we could work with thermometers adjusted to differences of tenths of a degree, or hundredths, or thousandths. (In a thought experiment there is scarcely any limit to the refinement of our instruments.) But then there would always be a next stage in refinement.

Another way of making things finer is to use a smaller and smaller thermometer. The smaller the thermometer, the less heat it will be able to take up or give off and the smaller the deviation from the truth that it will produce. By taking measurements with thermometers of different size, one might even be able to calculate what the temperature would be with a "zero-size" thermometer.

Of course, though, to make a true, ultimate calculation of the temperature with a zero-size thermometer, you must be able to read the temperatures given by the various finite-size thermometers with infinite exactness, and you can't do that.

In short, for various reasons, a perfectly exact measurement cannot be made, and there will always be a residual uncertainty, however small.

Of course, you can shrug this off as merely a philosophic point of no practical importance. You may not be able to make a measurement infinitely exact, but you can make it as exact as necessary. If the necessity for refinement sharpens, you need then only make sharper measurements. The uncertainty of your measurement will never be zero but (the old argument went) it can be made to approximate zero as closely as you wish.

This, however, is true only if it is taken for granted that you can make the effect on the measurement of the act of measurement itself very small. For this, the measuring device must be very small, or, at least, contain a very small component. But what if there is an ultimate limit to smallness and, if you try to measure some property of that ultimately small object, you must make use of a measuring device as big as itself, or bigger.

Then, too, suppose that in measuring one property of a system, you upset a second property; and that the closer and more accurate the measurement of the first, the more wildly disturbed is the second. To gain certainty in one place at the cost of gross uncertainty in another is no true gain.

Consider, for instance, the electron, which has a mass of $9.1 \times 10^{-28}$ grams. This is, as far as we know, a rock-bottom minimum to mass. No object that possesses mass at all possesses less mass than the electron.

Suppose, then, we want to measure some of the properties of an electron speeding by. With Laplace's great statement in mind, we want to determine the position and velocity of that electron at some given moment. If we do that there will still remain an enormous step to the ultimate goal of learning the position and velocity of *all* particles at one particular moment, but the longest

145

journey begins with but a single step. Let's concentrate on one electron to begin with.

The usual method of determining the position of anything is to receive light radiated by it, or to strike it with light and receive the reflection. In short, we see the object, and therefore know where it is.

An ordinary object is not appreciably affected by the light it reflects, but an electron is so small that it could be strenuously affected by that light. The idea, therefore, would be to use a very faint beam of light, one so faint that the electron would not be appreciably affected.

Unfortunately, there is a limit to light's faintness. Just as mass comes in thus-small-and-no-smaller units, so do all forms of energy. The least amount of light we can use is one photon, and if we try to send a photon of ordinary light at an electron, the wavelength associated with that photon is so long that it "steps over" the electron, and we can't see it.

We must use radiation of far shorter wavelength, an x ray or, better, a gamma ray, and receive the reflection by instruments. That is fine, but the shorter the wavelength, the greater the energy content of the photon. If a gamma-ray photon hits an electron, that electron might as well be kicked by a mule. It goes skittering off somewhere.

In other words, we may determine the position of the electron at a given moment, but the very act of that determination alters the velocity of that same electron at that same moment so that we cannot be sure what the velocity is.

Far more complicated thought experiments have been concocted and it turns out always that determining an electron's position alters its velocity and that determining an electron's velocity alters its position. A *simultaneous* determination of both properties, with the uncertainty in *each* as close to zero as you wish, turns out to be impossible. At least, no one has ever devised a thought experiment which would yield such simultaneous exactness. Even Einstein tried and even Einstein failed.

In 1927, the German physicist Werner Heisenberg formalized this view by announcing what he called the "uncertainty principle." This is now accepted as one of the fundamental generalizations of the physical universe; as fundamental, universal, and inescapable as a generalization can be. In fact, insofar as there can be certainty about anything at all in the universe, there is the certainty of uncertainty.

Heisenberg expressed the principle in an equation which we can work out as follows. Let's symbolize position as $p$ and momentum (which is equal to the mass of an object times its velocity) as $mv$. Uncertainty in a measurement is often expressed as the Greek capital "delta," which is just a triangle. The uncertainty in the measurement of position is therefore $\Delta p$ and that in the measurement of momentum is $\Delta mv$. The equation expressing Heisenberg's uncertainty principle is therefore:

$$(\Delta p)\ (\Delta mv) = \frac{h}{2\pi} \qquad \text{(Equation 1)}$$

The symbol, $h$, is Planck's constant, and $\pi$ (the Greek letter "pi") is the well-known ratio of the circumference of a circle to its diameter.

If we measure position in centimeters, mass in grams, and velocity in centimeters per second, then the approximate value of $h$ comes out to be $6.6256 \times 10^{-27}$ erg-seconds. The approximate value of $\pi$ is, of course, 3.1416. We can therefore express Equation 1 (very nearly) as:

$$(\Delta p)\ (\Delta mv) = 10^{-27} \qquad \text{(Equation 2)}$$

In a way, uncertainty arises out of the "graininess" of the universe; out of the fact that energy and mass come in packages of fixed size; that size being ultimately determined by the value of Planck's constant. If Planck's constant were equal to zero, there would be no uncertainty at all. If Planck's constant were quite large, matters would grow so uncertain that the universe would seem chaotic.

The situation is analogous to that of a newspaper photograph built up out of black and white dots, or a television picture built up out of closely spaced lines. The coarser the dots or the lines, the fuzzier the picture and the poorer the detail; the finer the dots or the lines, the clearer the picture and the sharper the detail.

The graininess of the universe as represented by Planck's constant is fine indeed, exceedingly fine; so fine that before the twentieth century, the graininess was never noticed. It had seemed that all measurements could be made as accurately as time and patience would permit and that, in principle, this accuracy could be made of unlimited closeness to the ultimate of zero uncertainty.

The question now is whether the graininess of the universe is so fine that even now, in the twentieth century, it might not be fine enough to ignore; whether it might not be a point of philosophic interest only and of no concern to practical men, or even to practical scientists.

Let's consider Equation 2 again. Heisenberg spoke of the uncertainty of the measurement of momentum rather than of velocity because as the velocity of an object increases, so does its mass, and the two are naturally treated together. However, mass alters appreciably only at very high velocities, and if velocities are kept below, say, a thousand miles a second, we can, without too great an error, consider the value of $m$ to be constant.

In that case we can deal with the uncertainty in velocity rather than momentum and write Equation 2 as:

$$(\Delta p)\,m\,(\Delta v) = 10^{-27} \quad \text{(Equation 3)}$$

Transposing $m$, we have:

$$(\Delta p)\,(\Delta v) = \frac{10^{-27}}{m} \quad \text{(Equation 4)}$$

Now we have an equation which tells us how to calculate the uncertainty in the simultaneous measurement of position and velocity of any particle, just the pair of measurements Laplace wanted to make. Under the circumstances outlined in Equation 4, we can see that we don't want to determine position *too* accurately for that will throw the measurement of velocity way off. Nor do we want to be too accurate about velocity at the expense of position. Let's make the healthy compromise of treating both position and velocity alike and making the measurements in such a way that the uncertainty in both cases is equal. We can do better with either one taken separately but we cannot possibly do better with both taken together.

Of the two measurements, that of position is the more dramatic. It is easy to see that we might not be certain of the exact velocity of an object, but surely (common sense tells us) we ought to know where it *is*, for heaven's sake. So, in Equation 4, let us let uncertainty in position equal uncertainty in velocity (numerically only, for the units will still differ) and let's represent both as $(\Delta p)$. That gives us:

$$(\Delta p)^2 = \frac{10^{-27}}{m} \quad \text{(Equation 5)}$$

or $$\Delta p = \frac{3.2 \times 10^{-14}}{\sqrt{m}} \quad \text{(Equation 6)}$$

We can put Equation 6 to work. We are dealing with measurements of mass in grams, so let's consider the

149

uncertainty involved in measuring the position and velocity of a 1-gram mass. (This is not a large mass; 1 gram is equal to about ½₈ of an ounce.)

If $m$ is set equal to 1, then the uncertainty in position comes out, according to Equation 6, to be $3.2 \times 10^{-14}$ centimeters. Another way of putting this uncertainty in position is 0.000000000000032 centimeters.

Modern techniques do not make it possible to measure the position of a gram weight that closely and no one in his right mind would need to measure it that closely for any practical purpose. However, it is important to remember that no matter how we refine our measurements, no matter how much time we take, how much ingenuity we expend, it is impossible to measure the position of a gram weight to an uncertainty of less than 0.000000000000032 centimeters; at least not without introducing a larger uncertainty in velocity; and it is *both* position and velocity that Laplace requires.

Yes, yes, you may say, but 0.000000000000032 centimeters is close enough. If we can get all the particles in the universe that closely positioned and velocitied, we can still stretch things far back into the past and far forward into the future.

Ah, but this unavoidable uncertainty of 0.000000000-000032 centimeters is for a 1-gram weight. If you look at Equation 6 you will see that as mass decreases the value of $\Delta p$ must increase. For instance, in Table 28, I have listed the uncertainties for a variety of objects that are considerably smaller than 1 gram in mass.

*Table 28—Some Uncertainties*

| OBJECT | APPROXIMATE MASS (GRAMS) | UNCERTAINTY OF POSITION (CENTIMETERS) |
|---|---|---|
| Ameba | $4 \times 10^{-6}$ | 0.000000000016 |
| Bacterium | $1 \times 10^{-12}$ | 0.000000032 |
| Gene | $4 \times 10^{-17}$ | 0.000005 |
| Uranium atom | $4 \times 10^{-22}$ | 0.0016 |

| Proton | $1.6 \times 10^{-24}$ | 0.025 |
| Electron | $9.1 \times 10^{-28}$ | 1.1 |

As you see, the graininess of the universe seems to be sufficiently fine for us to remain undisturbed by uncertainty even in the case of ordinary microscopic objects. If we measure the position of a bacterium down to an uncertainty of merely three hundred-millionths of a centimeter, surely we can't complain.

Only when we penetrate lower than the merely microscopic and approach the atomic and subatomic are we really in trouble. Only then does the uncertainty principle become something that can't be shrugged off as merely academic.

In fact, the situation is even worse at that lower end of the scale than it appears to be in Table 28. You might console yourself by saying that even a proton can be pinned down to within a fortieth of a centimeter, which isn't so awful, and that only the electron gives us trouble.

However, why use an arbitrary, unchangeable unit of length such as the centimeter? Why not adjust the unit to the object, by taking the object's own diameter as the measure of position? The reason for this is simple. If you yourself shift your position by a hundredth of a centimeter, this is unimportant and the ordinary observer will neither know nor care that you have moved. If, however, an ameba shifts its position by a hundredth of a centimeter, it moves the distance of its own diameter and anyone observing the ameba under a microscope would see the move and find it highly significant. So let's prepare Table 29.

*Table 29—More Uncertainties*

| OBJECT | APPROXIMATE DIAMETER (CENTIMETERS) | UNCERTAINTY OF POSITION (DIAMETERS) |
| --- | --- | --- |
| Ameba | 0.016 | 0.000000001 |
| Bacterium | 0.0001 | 0.0003 |
| Gene | 0.0000034 | 1.5 |

151

| Uranium | | |
|---|---|---|
| atom | 0.00000001 | 160,000 |
| Proton | 0.0000000000001 | 250,000,000,000 |
| Electron | 0.0000000000001 | 11,000,000,000,000 |

From this standpoint, affairs on the atomic and subatomic level are wildly uncertain, tremendously uncertain. If we try to ignore uncertainty on the atomic and subatomic level the results are simply grotesque. We cannot possibly view subatomic particles as tiny billiard balls because we can never pin down the position of such a tiny billiard ball. The best we can do (even if we are willing to increase the uncertainty in velocity tremendously) is to view it as a fuzzy object.

You might also speak of a particle that exists but that you can't detect as a particle, and to suppose that this particle has a particular probability of being here, or there, or in the other place. That is why it is so useful to consider particles as possessing wave-properties. Not only does the wave take up room and appear "fuzzy" but the equations that describe the waves also describe the probabilities of the particle being at this or that point in space.

The graininess of the universe is so coarse, relatively, at the subatomic level, that there is no way in which we can get a meaningful picture of atomic structure by using analogies from the ordinary world, where the graininess of the universe appears so fine that it can be ignored altogether. The best that can be done (and what I always do, for instance) is to advance misleading simplifications and hope they don't mislead too badly.

Of course, if the universe is grainy, it would be interesting to find evidence of the grains on a large scale, too, and not just among protons and electrons.

We can, indeed, imagine large-scale situations where the principle of uncertainty would make itself manifest. One such situation is described in an excellent book entitled *The Laws of Physics* by Milton A. Rothman (Basic Books, 1963).

Imagine, says Rothman, an enclosed box containing a perfect vacuum and two hard balls which are perfect spheres. The box is perfectly insulated so that there are no mechanical vibrations of any sort, no heat differences from point to point, nothing. The only force in the box is that of gravitation.

If one ball is fixed securely to the bottom of the box and the second ball is allowed to drop downward squarely on the apex of the fixed ball, then, by the classical laws of mechanics, the moving ball will bounce directly upward again, fall down upon the apex once more, bounce directly upward again and so on, for a great many times.

However, the principle of uncertainty would indicate that the ball could not *certainly* hit the exact apex, no matter how carefully it was aimed. And even if it did hit the exact apex, there could be no certainty that it would hit it again the next bounce. Once the position of strike varied from the apex by the tiniest amount, the moving ball would rise in a direction inclined by the tiniest degree to the vertical and would then strike the fixed ball even further from the apex on the next bounce and move up in a direction inclined even more to the vertical, and so on. After ten or twelve bounces, says Rothman, there would be a large probability that the moving ball would miss the fixed ball altogether, no matter how inhumanly carefully it had been aimed in the first place.

A similar situation involves a needle coming to a precise mathematical point. Imagine such a needle balanced on its point in a box free of vibration and heat differences and containing a perfect vacuum. The needle would only remain balanced on the mathematical point if its center of gravity were *exactly* over that point. But, by the principle of uncertainty, the center of gravity could only be within a certain distance of the direct-overheadness. As soon as it departed from direct-overheadness, however slightly, gravity would cause it to depart still further, and it would fall.

In short, the principle of uncertainty makes it impossible to balance a needle on a mathematical point, even under idealized and perfect conditions.

But these are imaginary situations. They involve large-scale objects, yes, but under conditions that cannot, in fact, be set up. Well, then, let's try something else.

As we generally tend to think of absolute zero, it is the temperature at which the energy of motion of atoms and molecules falls to zero. By that view, the vibration of atoms in any substance (all of which are solid in the neighborhood of absolute zero, one would think) slows to nothing and a deathlike and perfect immobility is all that is left.

But that is the view of classical physics, and not that of modern physics. Once the uncertainty principle is accepted, then we can't permit zero energy of motion at any time or under any conditions. If, at absolute zero, atoms were really and truly perfectly at rest, then we would know their velocity to be exactly zero. But we can't ever know velocity exactly. All we can say is that at absolute zero, the energy of atoms is within a certain very close distance to zero velocity, and that the atoms do continue to move, just a little bit.

This small residual 'zero point motion' which atoms and molecules retain even at absolute zero represents a *minimum* energy that cannot be removed without violating the inviolable uncertainty principle. For that reason, there can be no temperature lower than absolute zero. Nevertheless, energy content at absolute zero, while a minimum, is *not* zero.

Has this minimum energy any effect that can be observed? Yes, it does. The solid substance whose atoms are most easily jostled apart, and into liquid form, is solid helium. The minimum energy at absolute zero is sufficient for the purpose and the result is that under ordinary conditions, helium remains liquid *even at abso-lute zero*. Solid helium can only be formed under con-siderable pressure.

There, then, is a tangible effect of the uncertainty principle under large-scale conditions, and in the real world, not in some unattainable thought experiment.

Is this still too esoteric for you? Is absolute zero and liquid helium too specialized a display of the power of the uncertainty principle to be impressive?

How about this, then? If the uncertainty principle did not exist, neither would the universe as we know it; for the existence of all atoms other than hydrogen depends on the uncertainty principle.

But my space, alas, is used up. . . . Next chapter, please?

# 11. BEHIND THE TEACHER'S BACK

IN THE COURSE of writing these chapters in their original form, I have developed several bad habits. Partly, this is because I have a natural affinity for bad habits and partly because I am given such a free hand that it is hard not to pamper myself.

For instance, when space runs out and I am feeling Puckish, I commit a cliff-hanger and end wtih an indication that there is more to the story I am telling and that I will reserve the rest for some other time. Afterward, I may write that other column or I may not. It depends on my lordly whim.

A second bad habit is that of constantly referring to my genial audience as "Gentle Readers." The phrase originated, of course, as an indication that the readership was wellborn and possibly of noble descent. In our own egalitarian society, the phrase has lost its aristocratic connotation and one can't help but think of the Gentle Readers as being kindhearted, tender, and sweet. And so they are, so they are, but not always, I'm afraid.

My persistence in the first bad habit has just uncovered an exception to the generalization involved in my second bad habit.

In the original appearance of the previous chapter, I concluded with a cliff-hanger.

Within a matter of days, I received a letter from a

Fierce Reader.* Without a gentle word anywhere in it, she slashed away at me for having dared drop the subject of the uncertainty principle in the middle. "Is the continuation coming in the next issue?" she blazed.

I had to reply that it was not; that I hadn't given the matter much thought, and that I had thought that any time in the next year or two would be soon enough. However, since she sounded so savage, I thought I had better change my mind and write the continuation at once.

She replied with the smoldering threat of "You'd better!"

I hasten, dear lady, I hasten—

In order not to make things too dull, let's continue the story of the uncertainty principle by talking first of what seems to be a different subject altogether. This different subject we can call the Dilemma of the Atomic Nuclei that Shouldn't Be.

The New Zealand-born physicist Ernest Rutherford had conclusively demonstrated the existence of the atomic nucleus by 1911, and for twenty years after that its general structure seemed established. Atomic nuclei were considered to consist of two types of particles, protons and electrons, each of the former possessing a unit positive charge (+1) and each of the latter possessing a unit negative charge (−1). The protons, always present in excess, lent the nucleus a net positive charge.

The one exception to this general rule was the simplest nucleus of all, that of the more common hydrogen isotope. It consisted of a single particle, a proton, and nothing else.

As examples of more complicated situations, the most common oxygen isotope had atomic nuclei made up (it was thought) of 16 protons and 8 electrons for a net charge of +8; the most common iron isotope had

---

*A young lady—undoubtedly beautiful.

nuclei made up of 56 protons and 30 electrons for a net positive charge of +26; the most common uranium isotope had nuclei made up of 238 protons and 146 electrons for a net positive charge of +92; and so on.

This seemed to make sense. The protons in the nucleus, all of them positively charged, repelled each other on the well-known electrical principle that "like charges repel." However, if one placed electrons strategically among the protons, the attraction between protons and electrons (opposite charges attract) would neutralize the repulsions and allow the nucleus to hang together.

The electron could be considered a kind of "nuclear cement" and without it, it would seem, none of the nuclei could exist except that of hydrogen.

Physicists were, however, by no means happy with the atomic nuclei in all respects. By dint of shrewd calculations, they had decided that both protons and electrons had spins that could be characterized by the numbers $+\frac{1}{2}$ or $-\frac{1}{2}$. That meant that nuclei made up of even numbers of particles should have overall spins equal to the algebraic sum of an even number of halves, plus or minus. Such a sum would always have to be a whole number, such as 1, 2, or 3.

On the other hand, nuclei made up of an odd number of particles should have spins equal to the algebraic sum of an odd number of halves, and this should always add up to a "half-number" such as $1\frac{1}{2}$, $2\frac{1}{2}$, and $3\frac{1}{2}$.

Unfortunately it didn't work that way. As an example, consider the most common nitrogen isotope. It was made up (so physicists had decided in the Roaring Twenties) of 14 protons and 7 electrons for a total of 21 particles. Since this is an odd number of particles, the nitrogen nucleus ought to have an overall spin equal to a half-number, but it doesn't. Its spin is equal to a whole number.

Something was therefore seriously wrong. Either the nuclei did not have the structure they were thought to have or else the law of conservation of angular momentum was broken.

Physicists did not hesitate in their choice between these two alternatives. They have a peculiar affection for laws of conservation of this or that and would not willingly see one broken. Therefore, they began to turn looks of deep disfavor on the whole proton-electron theory of nuclear structure.

You can imagine, then, the thrill of exultation that swept the world of nuclear physics when, in 1932, the English physicist James Chadwick discovered the neutron, a particle that strongly resembled a proton except that it lacked an electric charge.

Scarcely allowing the neutron's discovery to grow cold, the German physicist Werner Karl Heisenberg (the same who, five years earlier, had enunciated the uncertainty principle) suggested that atomic nuclei were made up of protons and neutrons rather than protons and electrons.

Thus, the nuclei of the most common oxygen isotope would consist of 8 protons and 8 neutrons and its net charge would still be +8, thanks to the protons. (The neutrons, being uncharged, would contribute no charge of their own, and cancel none.) In the same way, the nuclei of the most common iron isotope would be made up of 26 protons and 30 neutrons (net charge, +26), the nuclei of the most common uranium isotope of 92 protons and 146 neutrons (net charge, +92), and so on.

The proton-neutron theory of nuclear structure could explain virtually all the facts of life concerning the nuclei, just as well as the proton-electron theory had been able to. In addition, it also fit the facts of nuclear spin with delightful accuracy. The nitrogen nucleus, for instance, by the new theory, was made up of 7 protons and 7 neutrons, for a total of 14 particles. Now it had an even total of particles and the overall spin could, with sense, be represented by a whole number.

159

The law of conservation of angular momentum was saved, by George.

There was just one gigantic fly in the ointment. According to the new theory, atomic nuclei other than those of hydrogen ought to be nonexistent.

The electron cement which had been counted upon to keep the protons in happy proximity was gone, and the protons were alone with their own company in the nucleus. (The neutrons were there, but electromagnetically speaking, they didn't count.) The nucleus was full of repulsion, a great deal of repulsion, and nothing but repulsion.

Within the nucleus, two protons are virtually in contact and are therefore separated, center to center, by about a ten-trillionth of a centimeter. The charge on each proton is terribly small by everyday standards, but the distance across which that charge need operate is terribly smaller. The result is that the repulsion between two neighboring protons works out to some 24,000,000 dynes.

This, needless to say, is a simply terrific force to be concentrated between a pair of objects as tiny as protons, and if this were the only force involved, two protons held in such close proximity would remain together for the merest split-instant and then separate at velocities close to that of light. Indeed, in 1932, there was no good way of accounting why two protons should be in such proximity in the first place.

Since in all atomic nuclei, save in that of the more common isotope of hydrogen, two or more nuclei *do* exist in such proximity (with neutrons strewn among them, of course), it turns out that there was nothing, in 1932, to account for the fact that matter, other than hydrogen, existed at all.

Yet even the cleverest and most inevitable scientific reasoning must bow before the presence of even the crudest fact. Matter *did* exist and consequently something was neutralizing and overcoming the repulsion between protons.

Unfortunately, that "something" had to be another force and there was a shortage of known forces. All the forces known in 1932 were produced by one or the other of just two types of "force-fields."

One of these was the "electromagnetic field," which governed the attractions and repulsions among protons and electrons. It is the presence of this field which keeps atoms from making actual contact, since at close approach the negatively charged electronic layers that fill the outskirts of one atom repel the negatively charged electronic layers that fill the outskirts of the other. Most ordinary forces with which we are acquainted—the pushes and pulls of everyday life—depend on the fact that the atoms of one piece of matter are, at close quarters, repelled by the atoms of another piece.

The only force known in 1932 which was not electromagnetic in nature was that of the "gravitational field," but it was quite clear that gravity could in no way counteract the mighty protonic repulsion within the nucleus. To be sure, protons within the nucleus experienced a gravitational attraction for each other since gravity depends only upon mass, is experienced only as an attraction, and is unaffected by electric charge. Unfortunately, however, the gravitational field is almost unimaginably weak; much less than a trillion-trillion-trillionth as strong as the electromagnetic field.

If the matter in a hundred billion galaxies (roughly all the matter in the known universe) could be squeezed into a volume no larger than the Earth, then the gravitational attraction of that mighty concentration of mass for a proton on its surface would equal the electromagnetic repulsion produced by a second proton in contact with the first.

But nothing less than a hundred billion galaxies crammed into an Earth-sized globe will do, and such objects are not to be found readily.

Something else is needed; some new type of force-field altogether. This would give us a "nuclear force" and if this is to hold nuclei together and make matter (other than hydrogen) possible, it must have certain properties. In the first place, it must be even stronger than the electromagnetic field, at least at close quarters, for it must produce an attraction between protons stronger than the electromagnetic repulsion between them.

Another point: Both electromagnetic and gravitational forces are long range. To be sure, they both weaken with distance, but only as the square of that distance. As a result, gravitational and electromagnetic forces can make themselves felt across vast gaps of space.

The hypothetical nuclear force can do no such thing. Within the infra-tiny nucleus it is overpoweringly intense, but it drops off very rapidly with distance; as a high power of that distance, not just the square. At a distance greater than a ten-trillionth of a centimeter (at greater widths than the diameter of an atomic nucleus, for instance) it becomes weaker than the electromagnetic force, and if the distance increases to two or three ten-trillionths of a centimeter it becomes indetectable.

Thus we can explain the fact that protons are strongly attracted at subnuclear distances, but show no signs of attraction if they are anything but cheek-by-jowl.

But we can't just invent a nuclear force of peculiar properties out of thin air. There's something about clear-cut observational evidence which is terribly desirable. To find some, let's go by way of the uncertainty principle. (See, I got there.)

In 1930, at a gathering of physicists at Brussels, Albert Einstein endeavored to show a fallacy in the reasoning that lay behind the uncertainty principle, then three years old. This principle held (as I explained in the previous chapter) that the inherent uncertainty in the determination of position multiplied by the inherent uncertainty in the determination of momentum was equal to not less than about one-sixth of Planck's constant:

$$(\Delta p)\ (\Delta mv) = 10^{-27} \qquad \text{(Equation 7)}$$

Einstein showed that if this were so then it was possible to maintain that the same relationship would hold for the product of the inherent uncertainty in the determination of energy content ($\Delta e$) and the inherent uncertainty in the determination of time ($\Delta t$) so that:

$$(\Delta e)\ (\Delta t) = 10^{-27} \qquad \text{(Equation 8)}$$

He then went on to describe a thought experiment in which both energy and time could be measured simultaneously with unlimited exactness, assuming one had perfect measuring tools. If Einstein were right, the uncertainty principle was out the window.

The Danish physicist Niels Bohr stayed awake that night, and the next day, haggard but triumphant, pointed out a few flaws in Einstein's reasoning, and showed that in the thought experiment under discussion, the determination of time would upset the determination of energy and vice versa. Einstein had to admit, reluctantly, that Bohr was right. The uncertainty principle has not been seriously challenged since.

Nevertheless, Einstein's version of the uncertainty principle, in which energy and time are linked, is perfectly correct and it introduces some interesting effects.

Using Einstein's version, imagine that you are measuring the energy content of some system at some instant of time. If your measurement pinpoints the energy content at some mathematical instant of time—over a duration of exactly zero seconds—you can't really measure the energy at all. The uncertainty of energy measurement is then infinite.

If you are content to say that the energy of the

system is thus and so over a certain period of time, then you are better off. The longer the period of time, the more exactly you can measure the energy content. Over a period of a ten-trillionth of a second or so, you could, ideally, measure the energy content of a system to a ten-trillionth of an erg or so. Under ordinary conditions, no one would want better than that.

Nevertheless, such a situation introduces a certain limited flexibility into the most important generalization known to science: the law of conservation of energy.

The law states that the energy content of a closed system must remain constant. Energy cannot appear out of nowhere and it cannot disappear into nowhere. However, if you measure the energy content of an atomic nucleus, let us say, over a period of a ten-trillionth of a second, you have determined that energy content, at best, only within a ten-trillionth of an erg. During that ten-trillionth of a second, the energy content can move freely up and down within that limit of a ten-trillionth of an erg, despite the law of conservation of energy. There would be no way of measuring that energy variation and therefore no way of accusing the nucleus of having broken the law.

You may say, of course, that it doesn't matter whether we can detect the violation of the law or not; that the law cannot be violated under any circumstances.

But is that so? Let's take an analogy.

Suppose a schoolboy is strictly forbidden to show any impoliteness to his stern teacher at any time under pain of a severe flogging. Suppose further that whenever the teacher turns his back, the boy sticks out his tongue but manages to get it in again before the teacher turns toward him. As nearly as the teacher can tell, the boy is being perfectly polite at all times, and is not breaking the rule.

In other words, a rule which ordinarily can't be broken, can be broken if it is done so over a short enough period. We can make this plain if we reword the rule to make it conform not to an impossible idealism, but to the situation as it truly exists. The rule is not: "A schoolboy must never be impolite to his teacher!" The rule, very obviously, is: "A schoolboy must never be caught being impolite to his teacher." All human rules are of that form. Even a murderer goes unpunished if the existence of the murder goes unsuspected.

Analogously, we must not define the law of conservation of energy as: "The total energy of a system remains constant at all times" but only as: "The total energy of a system remains measurably constant at all times."

What we cannot measure, we cannot expect to insist on controlling by fiat, and the uncertainty principle tells us what we cannot measure. Energy is permitted to vary by a certain fixed amount, and the shorter the time interval over which this variation takes place, the greater the amount of variation permitted.

How does this apply to the nuclear field?

Again we return to Heisenberg. When he suggested the proton-neutron structure of the nucleus he saw very well the difficulty that arose in connection with protonic repulsion. He suggested that force-fields exerted their influences of attraction and repulsion by the exchange of particles between one body and another. In the case of the electromagnetic field, the particle exchanged was the photon (the unit of radiant energy); and in the case of the gravitational field, the particle exchanged was the graviton (a particle which remains as yet hypothetical for it has never been detected).

If there is to be a third force-field, a nuclear one, there must be a third exchange particle.

The Japanese physicist Hideki Yukawa got to work on the properties of this hypothetical nuclear exchange particle.

This exchange particle existed by virtue of the loophole offered by the uncertainty principle. It contained energy, but only the amount permitted by that principle.

165

The shorter the time during which the nuclear exchange particle existed, the more energy it might have, so it was necessary to fix the duration of its existence somehow.

The exchange particle had to exist long enough to get from one proton to its neighbor within the nucleus and back or it would not exist long enough to set up an attractive force between protons. It could not exist much longer than that because then it would last long enough to get outside the nucleus and make the nuclear force felt there—in regions where the nuclear force was never felt. Thus the time of duration, and therefore the particle's energy content, could be determined within rather fine limits.

Suppose the exchange particle traveled at the velocity of light. It could then cover the distance from one proton to a neighboring proton and back in about 0.000000000000000000000005, or $5 \times 10^{-24}$ seconds.

If an energy measurement is made over a time interval not less than $5 \times 10^{-24}$ seconds, the additional energy made available for the briefly existing exchange particle, by the flexibility introduced into the law of conservation of energy by the uncertainty principle, can be determined.

Turning to Einstein's version of the uncertainty principle, the uncertainty in time ($\Delta t$) is set equal to $5 \times 10^{-24}$ and Equation 8 becomes:

$$(\Delta e) \ (5 \times 10^{-24}) = 10^{-27} \qquad \text{(Equation 9)}$$

Solving for $\Delta e$, we find that it equals 0.0002 ergs. This is the amount of energy that the uncertainty principle makes available for the exchange particle of the nuclear field. It is a tremendous amount of energy for a single particle and it would be difficult to handle as pure energy. It would be more convenient if the energy were, for the most part, packed into the form of mass—which is the most condensed form of energy known. An amount of energy equal to 0.0002 ergs can be packed into a particle with a mass about 250 times that of an electron, with enough left over to give it a velocity nearly that of light.

Yukawa, when he published his theory in 1935, suggested therefore that the nuclear exchange particle have mass (unlike the massless photon and graviton) and that the mass be intermediate between that of the electron on one hand and the proton and neutron on the other. (The proton and neutron are roughly 1,840 times as massive as the electron and, therefore, something over 7 times as massive as Yukawa's exchange particle.)

Suggesting a nuclear exchange particle of specific properties is one thing, but some observational evidence was still necessary. Inside the nucleus, the exchange particle comes and goes within the time limit set by the uncertainty principle. This means it cannot be observed under any circumstances. It is a "virtual particle," not a real one.

But suppose energy is added to the nucleus; enough energy to supply the amount required for the exchange particle without having to resort to the flexibility of the uncertainty principle. In that case, might not the exchange particle assume a real existence and condescend to hang around long enough to allow itself to be detected?

The catch was that packing the necessary energy into the small confines of the nucleus isn't easy. In the 1930s, the only possible source of sufficiently concentrated energy were the cosmic rays. In 1936, the American physicist Carl David Anderson, in the course of his cosmic ray studies, found that cosmic rays were indeed occasionally knocking particles out of the nucleus that resembled Yukawa's exchange particle in mass. That mass turned out to be 207 times that of an electron.

Anderson called the particle a "mesotron," from the Greek word *meso* meaning "intermediate," but this was quickly abbreviated to "meson."

Unfortunately, Anderson's meson did not have the properties expected of Yukawa's exchange particle. For one thing, Yukawa's exchange particle had to interact strongly with atomic nuclei, but Anderson's meson did not do so. It virtually ignored the existence of nuclei. The disappointment among physicists was keen.

Then, in 1948, a group of English physicists, headed by Cecil Frank Powell, who were studying cosmic rays in the Bolivian Andes, detected another particle of intermediate mass. The new particle was about 270 times as massive as the electron (about a third more massive than Anderson's particle), and it interacted with nuclei with a most gratifying avidity.

The new particle was also called a meson and it was distinguished from the meson earlier discovered by means of Greek letter prefixes. Anderson's meson was "mu-meson," soon shortened to "muon"; while Powell's meson was a "pi-meson," soon shortened to "pion." It is the pion that is Yukawa's exchange particle.

It is the pion whose existence within the nucleus makes possible the development of a nuclear force of attraction between neighboring protons over a hundred times as intense as the electromagnetic force of repulsion between them. It is the pion therefore that makes the existence of matter, other than hydrogen, possible. And the existence of the pion is itself made possible (behind the teacher's back, so to speak) by the uncertainty principle.

—So be careful how you yearn for certainty.

And what about the muon? If that is not the exchange particle, what is it? That, as it happens, is an interesting question, for in recent years the muon has raised two problems that are possibly the most fascinating that currently face the nuclear physicist. It is not even a meson, really. It is, instead—

But my space, alas, is used up. . . . Next chapter please?

# 12. THE LAND OF MU

WHEN I was in my early teens, I found a book in the public library that seemed fascinating. It was *The Lost Continent of Mu* by James Churchward and I took it out exultantly.

The disappointment was keen. I may have been young, but I wasn't so young as not to recognize nonsense. This was my first encounter with the "serious" literature spawned by the Atlantis legend (as opposed to honest science fiction) and I needed no second.

If you want to know more about the Atlantis myth, about Lemuria and Mu, and so on, don't look for it here. I refer you to an amusing and interesting book by a gentleman with the highest rationality-quotient I have ever met: *Lost Continents* by L. Sprague de Camp (Gnome Press, 1954).

For myself, I will go no further into the subject except to say that the Land of Mu was a hypothetical continent that filled the Pacific Ocean and that, like Atlantis, allegedly sank beneath the waves, after having supposedly harbored a high civilization.

Utter bilge, of course, and yet there is a queer co-incidence that crops up.

Churchward could not have known, when he wrote his first book on Mu in 1926, that the time would come when the word "Mu" would gain a certain significance in science. This significance rests chiefly in the problems that have arisen in connection with "Mu." These problems, far from being solved, or even moving toward

169

solution, have, in the last quarter century, grown steadily more puzzling and intense until now, in the mid-sixties, the daintiest and most succulent enigmas of the nuclear physicist rest right on "Mu."

There *is* a Land of Mu, in a manner of speaking, and it is far more fascinating and mysterious than the murky lost continent of Churchward's fog-ridden imagination.

Let me tell you about the real Land of Mu, Gentle Readers—

As usual, I will start at the beginning; and the beginning, in this case, is the previous chapter, where I described the efforts made to account for the existence of atomic nuclei despite the strong mutual repulsion of the protons contained in those nuclei. Let me repeat just a little.

To allow the nucleus to exist, the Japanese physicist Hideki Yukawa had found it necessary to postulate the existence of a particle intermediate in mass between the proton and the electron. In 1936, such a particle was found and was promptly named the "mesotron" from the Greek word *mesos* meaning "in the middle" or "intermediate." A syllable was saved by shortening this name to "meson."

Unfortunately, there were two flaws to this happy discovery. The first was that the meson was just a little on the light side. This, however, might not be serious. It might easily turn out that there were factors Yukawa hadn't correctly taken into account in his reasoning.

The second flaw was less easily dismissed. The whole point of the meson was that if it were to serve as the "cement" of the atomic nucleus, it would have to interact very rapidly with the protons and neutrons within that nucleus. It should, indeed, react with a proton, for instance, in not much more than a trillionth of a trillionth of a second. A stream of mesons striking a group of nuclei ought to be gulped up at once.

But this didn't happen. A stream of mesons, shooting

forward at great energies, can pass through inches of lead. In doing so, the mesons must carom off vast numbers of atomic nuclei and not be absorbed by any of them.

For a dozen years, that irritated physicists. A particle had been predicted; it was found; and it proved not to be the particle that was predicted. Fortunately, in 1948, a second meson was found, a little more massive than the first, and it *did* react virtually instantaneously with nuclei. The second meson checked out perfectly as Yukawa's predicted particle and physicists have had no cause to question that conclusion since.

It was now necessary to distinguish between the two mesons by name, and one good way was to make use of Greek letter prefixes, a common habit in science.

For instance, the first meson had precedence to the right to have the prefix "m" for "meson." The Greek letter equivalent of "m" is $\mu$ which, in English, is called "mu."* Therefore, the first meson, the one which is *not* Yukawa's particle, was named the "mu-meson" and that is more and more frequently being abbreviated to "muon."

The second meson, which *is* Yukawa's particle, was first discovered among the products of cosmic ray bombardment (the "primary radiation") of the upper atmosphere. It therefore should have the initial "p" for "primary." The Greek letter equivalent of "p" is $\pi$ which, in English, is called "pi." Therefore, Yukawa's particle became the "pi-meson" or "pion."

Suppose, now, we set the mass of the electron at 1, and consider the masses of the two mesons and of the proton and neutron, as in Table 30.

*This continent of Mu, concerning which Churchward wrote, has no connection at all with the Greek letter mu, but I am building this article on the coincidence all the same.

*Table 30—The Masses of Subatomic Particles*

| electron | 1 |
|----------|-----------|
| muon     | 206.77    |
| pion     | 273.2     |
| proton   | 1836.12   |
| neutron  | 1838.65   |

If we look at this group of particles, we can say that the atom is made up of a nucleus, containing protons and neutrons held together by pions, and that outside that nucleus are to be found electrons. Here are four different particles, all essential to atomic structure.

But that leaves the muon; the mu-meson; the particle which we can name, if we are feeling romantic enough, the physicists' "Land of Mu." What does it do? What function does it serve?

Do you know that it is just about thirty years now since the muon was discovered and physicists still don't know what it does or what function it serves.

This puzzle—the first of the Land of Mu—is not as acute as it might be. In the 1950s and 1960s, other particles were discovered by the dozens. There then arose the question of accounting for the existence and function of a large number of particles and not the muon only.

There is the feeling now that what is needed is a general theory covering subatomic particles as a whole. Indeed such general theories are now being advanced, but this chapter is not the place to discuss them.

However, other problems arose in connection with the muon that apply strictly to the muon and to no other particle; and concerning which physicists haven't yet the foggiest beginning of an answer.

Suppose we compare the muon and the electron, for instance.

Item 1: The electron carries a negative electric charge, arbitrarily set equal to unit-size, so that its charge is described as —1. It has a positively charged twin, the positron (charge, +1). There is, however, no such thing as a "neutral electron" (charge, 0).

Should there be? Well, there is a "neutral proton" (charge, 0), which we call a neutron, which is a trifle more massive than a proton (charge, +1) or its twin, the anti-proton (charge, —1). There is a neutral pion (charge, 0), which is a trifle less massive than the positive pion (charge, +1) or its twin, the negative pion (charge, —1).

Nevertheless, although the proton and pion can exist in uncharged form, the electron apparently cannot. At least a neutral electron has never been detected and there is no theoretical reason to suspect that it might exist.

Now the muon. There is a negative muon (charge, —1) and a positive muon (charge, +1) but there is no neutral muon.

Indeed, in May 1965 (three days ago, as I write this), the results of an experiment were announced in which streams of muons and of electrons were bounced off protons. From the nature of the scattering one could calculate the volume over which the electric charge of a muon and of an electron were spread. No difference could be detected in the two particles. We can conclude then that in terms of nature and distribution of charge, the muon and electron are indistinguishable.

Item 2: Subatomic particles have a property which can be most easily described as spin about an axis. The spin of an electron (or positron) can be expressed as either +½ or —½. The spin of a muon (either negative or positive) can also be expressed as either +½ or —½. In terms of spin, then, the muon and electron are indistinguishable.

Item 3: The spin of the electron (or positron) sets up a magnetic field whose strength can be expressed as 1.001160 Bohr magnetons. The spin of the muon (either negative or positive) sets up a magnetic field of strength equal to 1.001162 Bohr magnetons. The difference is quite unimportant and in terms of magnetism, too, then, the muon and electron are just about indistinguishable.

Item 4: The electron and muon can take part (or fail to take part) in certain interactions with other particles. For instance:

a) A pion is an unstable particle which, left to itself, breaks down in a couple of hundredths of a microsecond.* When it breaks down, it may produce a muon and a neutrino; or it may produce an electron and a neutrino.** In brief, either an electron or a negative muon can be produced by the breakdown of a negative pion; either a positron or a positive muon can be produced by the breakdown of a positive pion.

b) An electron has very little tendency to interact with atomic nuclei; it tends to remain outside the nucleus. A muon has very little tendency to interact with atomic nuclei; it tends to remain outside the nucleus. In fact, negative muons can replace electrons in their orbits about nuclei, producing what are called "mesonic atoms." No doubt, positive muons could replace positrons in their orbits about the nuclei of anti-matter to produce "anti-mesonic atoms."

c) It is possible for an electron and its positively charged twin, the positron, to circle each other for short intervals of time, making up a neutral system called "positronium." It is also possible for the electron to circle a positive muon in place of the positron, to form "muonium." Undoubtedly, a positron can circle a negative muon to form "anti-muonium," and a negative muon can circle a positive muon to form something for which, as far as I know, no name has yet been coined ("mumuonium"?).

We can conclude then that as far as the nature of

*A microsecond is equal to a millionth of a second, or $10^{-6}$ seconds.
**I'll have something to say about neutrinos later in the article.

particle interactions in which electrons and muons can take part is concerned, the two are indistinguishable.

In fact, as physicists examined the muon more and more thoroughly through the 1950s, it began to dawn upon them that the muon and electron were identical.

Well, almost identical. There remained two important points of difference.

The first involves the matter of stability. The electron and positron are each stable. An electron or a positron, alone in the universe, will never (as far as we know) alter its nature and become anything else.

The muon, however, is unstable. Even if alone in the universe, it will break down, after an average lifetime of 2.2 microseconds. The negative muon will break down to an electron and a couple of neutrinos, while a positive muon will break down to a positron and a couple of neutrinos.

This certainly seems to be a tremendous distinction between electron and muon, but, oddly enough, it isn't. A microsecond is a brief interval of time on the human scale but not on the subatomic scale. On the subatomic scale there are reactions and breakdowns that take place in $10^{-23}$ seconds. The pion interactions that serve to hold an atomic nucleus together take place in such an interval of time.

If we take $10^{-23}$ seconds as a normal interval of time on the subatomic scale; short but not extraordinarily short; we might compare it to 1 second on the human scale. In that case $10^{-6}$ seconds, which is a hundred quadrillion times as long as $10^{-23}$ seconds, would be the equivalent of three billion years on the human scale. If we consider the muon from the viewpoint of the subatomic world, it lasts billions of years and surely that is "practically forever."

The difference between an electron that lasts forever and a muon that lasts practically forever is not great enough to bother a physicist.

You yourself may, however, feel more hardheaded than a physicist. "Practically forever" is not "forever" you may exclaim, and six billion years is not eternity.

In that case, look at it another way. When subatomic particles break down, the tendency is to form a lighter particle, provided none of the rules of the game are broken. Thus, when a negatvie muon breaks down it forms the negatively charged, but lighter electron. The mass decreases but the electric charge remains, for the rules of the game decree that electric charge may not vanish.

The electron, however, cannot break down for there is no particle less massive than itself that carries an electric charge. The charge must remain and therefore the electron, willy-nilly, must remain.

The positron remains stable, too, because there is no particle less massive than itself that carries a positive electric charge.

(Of course, an electron and a positron can undergo mutual annihilation, for the negative charge of the first cancels the positive charge of the second. The total charge of the two particles before annihilation is $+1-1$, or 0, so that no *net* charge is destroyed.)

In short, the fact that the electron lasts forever and the negative muon lasts only practically forever is entirely a matter of the difference in mass. We can ignore the difference in stability, then, as a purely derivative matter and pass on to the difference in mass, which seems essential.

The negative muon is 206.77 times as massive as the electron; the positive muon is 206.77 times as massive as the positron. Up through 1962, all other differences between these two sets of particles seemed to stem directly from this difference in mass.

The case of stability versus instability is a case in point. Here is another. When a meson replaces an electron in its orbit about an atomic nucleus, to form

THE LAND OF MU

a mesonic atom, the meson must have the same angular momentum as the electron. The angular momentum increases with mass and also with distance from the center of rotation. Since the meson is over 200 times as massive as the electron, it must make up for that increased mass by decreasing its distance from the center of rotation (the nucleus) correspondingly. In very massive atoms, which ordinarily draw their innermost electrons into close quarters indeed, the meson, drawn closer still, actually circles within the nucleus's outer perimeter. The fact that the muon can circle freely within the nucleus shows how small the tendency is for the muon to interact with protons or neutrons. (It also raises puzzling questions as to the nature of the inner structure of the nucleus.)

In addition, the electrons of an atom, in shifting from energy level to energy level, typically emit or absorb photons of visible light. The more massive meson shifts over energy gaps that are correspondingly greater. The photons such atoms emit or absorb are over 200 times as energetic as those of visible light and are in the x-ray region.

The peculiar structure of a mesonic atom and its ability to emit or absorb x rays can thus be seen to be merely another consequence of the great mass of the muon.

Here is still another example. A pion, in breaking down, can form either a muon or an electron. One might think that, if the muon and electron were exactly alike, each ought to form with equal probability and as many electrons as muons ought to be formed.

This, however, is not so. For every electron formed, seven thousand muons are formed. Why is that?

According to the theory of such interactions, the probability with which a muon or an electron is formed depends on how far short of the speed of light the speed of the particle formed happens to be. The electron

177

is a very light particle and at the moment of formation is fired out at almost the speed of light. Its speed is only slightly less than the speed of light and the probability of its formation is correspondingly small.

The muon, however, is over two hundred times as massive as the electron and is therefore considerably more sluggish. Its velocity, when formed, is quite a bit less than the speed of light and the probability of its formation rises correspondingly. The difference between the quantity of muons formed in pion breakdown and the quantity of electrons again boils down to a consequence of the difference in mass.

Physicists have therefore taken to looking at the negative muon as nothing more than a "massive electron" and at the positive muon as a "massive positron."

And that is the second puzzle from the physicists' Land of Mu. Why should the muon be so much more massive than the electron? And just 206.77 times as massive, no more or less? No one knows.

For that matter, why should this huge difference in mass make so little difference in respect to charge, spin, magnetic field, and type of interactions undergone? No one knows.

And even yet we are not done. I've saved the most recent and most tantalizing puzzle for last.

There are certain massless, chargeless particles called neutrinos which have, as their twins, anti-neutrinos. (They are opposite in terms of the direction of their magnetic fields.) These particles are particularly associated with electrons and positrons.

When an electron is formed in the course of a particle breakdown, an anti-neutrino is formed along with it. When a positron is formed, a neutrino is formed along with it.

When a negative muon is formed in the course of a particle breakdown, an anti-neutrino is formed along with it, too. And, of course, when a positive muon is formed, there comes the neutrino.

At first it was thought that since the muon was more massive than the electron, the neutrino produced along with muons ought to be more massive than those produced along with electrons. Consequently, physicists distinguished among them by speaking of a "neutretto" as being associated with muons.

However, the closer they looked at the "neutretto," the less massive it seemed to be until, finally, they decided the "neutretto" was massless.

But the only difference between muon and electron was mass, and if that difference was wiped out between the neutretto of one and the neutrino of the other, there was no difference left in the latter case.

Both were neutrinos (and anti-neutrinos). Physicists decided then that the muon's neutrino (and anti-neutrino) and the electron's neutrino (and anti-neutrino) were the same particle in every respect. This seemed but another example of how the electron and muon could not be distinguished except by mass and mass-derived properties.

Yet one problem remained. When a negative muon broke down, it formed an electron and *two* neutrinos. From theoretical considerations, it was necessary to consider one of those neutrinos a neutrino and the other an anti-neutrino.

But a neutrino and an anti-neutrino should be able to annihilate each other and leave nothing behind but electromagnetic radiation. In that case, a negative muon should break down to form an electron as the only particle. And a positive muon should break down to form a positron as the only particle. At least, this should be observed once in a while.

However, it was *never* observed. The neutrino and anti-neutrino were always formed in the breakdown of either the negative or positive muon and never annihilated each other. Physicists began to wonder if perhaps the neutrino and anti-neutrino didn't annihilate each other because they *couldn't* annihilate each other. Perhaps there were two kinds of neutrinos and two kinds of anti-neutrinos after all, one set associated with electrons and one with muons, and perhaps the neutrino of one set could not annihilate the anti-neutrino of the other set.

Could it be then that a negative muon broke down to form 1) an electron, 2) an electron-anti-neutrino, and 3) a muon-neutrino? And could a positive muon break down to form 1) a positron, 2) an electron-neutrino, and 3) a muon-anti-neutrino?

If so, that would explain the facts of muon breakdown. Nevertheless, the possibility of two kinds of neutrinos seemed too much to swallow without additional evidence.

In 1962, therefore, at Brookhaven, Long Island, a "two-neutrino experiment" was set up and carried out. High-energy protons were smashed into a beryllium target under conditions that formed a high-energy stream of positive and negative pions. These broke down almost at once to positive and negative muons. The positive muons, when formed, were accompanied by muon-neutrinos, while the negative muons, when formed, were accompanied by muon-anti-neutrinos.

Before the muons had a chance to break down, the stream struck a wall of armor plate about forty-five feet thick. All pions and muons were stopped, but the muon-neutrinos and muon-anti-neutrinos went right on through. (Neutrinos can pass through light-years of solid matter without being stopped.)

On the other side of the armor plate, the neutrinos and anti-neutrinos had a chance to interact with particles. They did this only very rarely, but every once in a while one of them did. A neutrino (charge, 0) could strike a neutron (charge, 0), for instance, and form a proton (charge, +1).

The rules of the game, however, say that you can't form a positive electric charge out of nothing. If one is formed, then a particle with a negative electric charge must be formed simultaneously so as to keep the total charge zero.

Therefore when a neutrino and neutron combine to form a proton, they must also form either an electron or a negative muon, since either of them can supply the necessary charge of −1 to balance the proton's +1.

All the neutrinos in question were formed along with muons and are therefore muon-neutrinos. If the muon-neutrinos were indeed different from electron-neutrinos, then only muons should be formed. If the muon-neutrinos were identical with electron-neutrinos, then the neutrinos could be considered as associated with either, and some of each ought to be formed. They might not be formed in equal numbers, for the mass difference might apply, but they both ought to be formed.

However, in the first experiment and in all that followed, muons, and muons only, have been formed. Electrons have never been observed.

The conclusion is that there are indeed two different neutrino/anti-neutrino pairs; one pair associated with electrons and positrons, and one pair associated with negative and positive muons.

And there is the third puzzle from the physicists' Land of Mu. What in blazes is the difference between a muon-neutrino and an electron-neutrino?

Both are massless. Both are chargeless. Both have a spin of ½. Put each in isolation and the physicist cannot imagine how to distinguish one from the other.

But the neutron can tell. It will interact with one of them to form a proton and a muon, and with the other to form a proton and an electron. And how does the neutron tell the two neutrinos apart when we can't?

No one knows.

181

There you have the physicists' Land of Mu. Compare all this with Churchward's Land of Mu, which could produce nothing more than the imaginary sinking of a mythical continent, and tell me where the true romance lies.

# PART III

❧

# — HEAVEN.

# 13. TIME AND TIDE

WHAT WITH ONE THING and another, I've gotten used to explaining various subtle puzzles that arise in connection with the scientific view of the universe. For instance, I have disposed of the manner in which electrons and photons can be waves part of the time and particles the rest of the time in a dozen different ways and by use of a dozen different analogies.

I've gotten so good at it, in fact, that at dinner parties the word nervously goes about, "For heaven's sake, don't ask Asimov anything about wave-particle duality."

And no one ever does. I sit there all primed and aching to explain, and no one ever asks. It kills the party for me.

But it's the simple thing that throws me. I've just been trying to write a very small book on the Moon for third-graders and as part of the task I was asked to explain why there are two high tides each day.

Simple, I thought, and a condescending smirk passed over my face. I flexed my fingers and bent over the typewriter.

As the time passed, the smirk vanished and the hair at my temples grew perceptibly grayer. I managed at last, after a fashion, but if you don't mind, Gentle Reader, I'd like to try again. I need the practice.

The tides have bothered people for a long time, but not the good old Greeks, with reference to whom I start so many articles. The Greeks, you see, lived (and still live, for that matter) on the shores of the Mediterranean Sea. That sea happens to be relatively tideless because it is so nearly landlocked that high tide can't get through the Strait of Gibraltar before the time for it has passed and it is low tide again.

About 325 B.C., however, a Greek explorer, Pytheas of Massalia (the modern Marseilles), ventured out of the Mediterranean and into the Atlantic. There he came across good pronounced tides, with two periods of high water each day and two periods of low water in between. Pytheas made good observations of these, undoubtedly helped out by the inhabitants of the shores facing the open ocean who were used to the tides and took them for granted.

The key observation was that the range between high water and low water was not always the same. It increased and decreased with time. Each month there were two periods of particularly large range between high and low tides ("spring tides") and, in between, two periods of particularly small range ("neap tides").

What's more, the monthly variations matched the phases of the Moon. The spring tides came at full Moon and new Moon, while the neap tides came at first quarter and third quarter. Pytheas suggested, therefore, that the tides were caused by the Moon. Some of the later Greek astronomers accepted this, but for the most part, Pytheas's suggestion lay fallow for two thousand years.

There were plenty of men who believed that the Moon influenced the manner in which crops grew, the rationality or irrationality of men, the way in which a man might turn into a werewolf, the likelihood of encountering spooks and goblins—but that it might influence the tides seemed to be going a bit far!

I suspect that one factor that spoiled the Moon/tide connection for thoughtful scholars was precisely the fact that there were two tides a day.

For instance, suppose there is a high tide when the Moon is high in the sky. That would make sense. The

Moon might well be drawing the water to itself by some mysterious force. No one in ancient and medieval times had any notion of just how such a force might behave, but one could at least give it a name such as "sympathetic attraction." If the water heaped up under a high Moon, a point on the rotating Earth, passing through the heap, would experience a high tide followed by a low tide.

But a little over twelve hours later, there would be another high tide and then the Moon would be nowhere in the sky. It would be, in fact, on the other side of the globe, in the direction of a man's feet. If the Moon were exerting a sympathetic attraction, the water on the man's side of the globe ought to be pulled downward in the direction of his feet. There ought to be a hollow in the ocean, not a heap.

Or could it be that the Moon exerted a sympathetic attraction on the side of the Earth nearest itself and a sympathetic repulsion on the side opposite. Then there would be a heap on both sides, two heaps all told. In one rotation of the Earth, a point on the shore would pass through both heaps and there would be two high tides each day, with two low tides in between.

The notion that the Moon would pull in some places and push in other places must have been very hard to accept, and most scholars didn't try. So the Moon's influence on the tides was put down to astrological superstition by the astronomers of early modern times.

In the early 1600s, for instance, Johannes Kepler stated his belief that the Moon influenced the tides, and the sober Galileo laughed at him. Kepler, after all, was an astrologer who believed in the influence of the Moon and the planets on all sorts of earthly phenomena and Galileo would have none of that. Galileo thought the tides were caused by the sloshing of the oceans back and forth as the Earth rotated—and he was quite wrong.

Came Isaac Newton at last! In 1685, he advanced the law of universal gravitation. By using that law it became obvious that the Moon's gravitational field had to exert an influence on the Earth and the tides could well be a response to that field.

But why *two* tides? What difference does it make whether we call the force exerted by the Moon on the Earth "sympathetic attraction" or "gravitational attraction"? How could the Moon, when it was on the other side of the Earth, cause the water on this side to heap upward, *away* from the Moon. The Moon would still have to be pulling in one place and pushing in another, wouldn't it? And that still wouldn't make sense, would it?

Ah, but Newton did more than change words and substitute "gravity" for "sympathy." Newton showed exactly how the gravitational force varied with distance, which was more than anyone before him had shown in connection with the vaguely postulated sympathetic force.

The gravitational force varied inversely as the square of the distance. That means the force grows smaller as the distance grows larger; and if the distance increases by a ratio of $\chi$, the force decreases by a ratio of $\chi^2$.

Let's take the specific case of the Moon and the Earth. The average distance of the Moon's center from the surface of the Earth nearest itself is 234,000 miles. In order to get the distance of the Moon's center from the surface of the Earth farthest from itself, you must add the thickness of the Earth (8,000 miles) to the first figure, and that gives you 242,000 miles.

If we set the distance of the Moon to the near surface of the Earth at 1, then the distance to the far surface is 242,000/234,000 or 1.034. As the distance increases from 1.000 to 1.034, the gravitational force decreases from 1.000 to $1/1.034^2$, or 0.93.

There is thus a 7.0 percent difference in the amount of gravitational force exerted by the Moon on the two sides of the Earth.

If the Earth were made of soft rubber, you might

picture it as yielding somewhat to the Moon's pull, but each part would yield by a different amount depending on the strength of the pull on that particular part.

The surface of the Earth on the Moon's side would yield most since it would be most strongly attracted. The parts beneath the surface would be attracted with a progressively weaker force and move less and less toward the Moon. The opposite side of the Earth, being farthest from the Moon would move toward it least of all.

There would therefore be two bulges; one on the part of the Earth's surface nearest the Moon, since that part of the surface would move the most; and another on the part of the Earth's surface farthest from the Moon, since that part of the surface would move the least and lag behind all the rest of the Earth.

If that's not clear, let's try analogy. Imagine a compact group of runners running a long race. All of them run toward the finish line so that we might suppose some "force" is attracting them toward that finish line. As they run, the speedier ones pull out ahead and the slower ones fall behind. Despite the fact that only one "force" is involved, a "force" directed toward the finish line, there are two "bulges" produced; a bulge of runners extending forward toward the finish line in the direction of the force, and another bulge of runners extending backward in the direction opposite to that of the force.

Actually the solid body of the Earth, held together by strong intermolecular forces, yields only very slightly to the gravitational differential exerted by the Moon on the Earth. The liquid oceans, held together by far weaker intermolecular forces, yield considerably more and make two "tidal bulges," one toward the Moon and one away from it.

As the Earth rotates, an individual point on some seacoast is carried past the first tidal bulge and then half a day later through the second. There are thus two high tides and two low tides in one complete rotation of the Earth—or, to put it more simply, in one day.

If the Moon were motionless, the tidal bulges would always remain in exactly the same place, and high tides would be exactly twelve hours apart. The Moon moves in its orbit about the Earth, however, in the same direction that the Earth rotates, and the tidal bulges move with it. By the time some point on Earth has passed through one bulge and is approaching a second, that second bulge has moved onward so that the Earth must rotate an additional half hour in order to pass the point under question through high tide again.

The time between high tides is twelve hours and twenty-five minutes, and the time from one high tide to the next but one is twenty-four hours and fifty minutes. Thus, the high tides each day come nearly one hour later than on the day before.

But why spring tides and neap tides and what is the connection between tides and the phases of the Moon?

For that we have to bring in the Sun. It, too, exerts a gravitational influence on the Earth. The gravitational pull of two separate heavenly bodies on the Earth varies directly with the mass of the bodies in question and inversely with the square of their distance from the Earth.

To make things simple, let's use the mass of the Moon as the mass-unit, and the average distance of the Moon from the Earth (center to center) as the distance-unit. The Moon possesses 1 Moon-mass and is at 1 Moon-distance in other words, and the Moon's gravitational pull upon us can therefore be set at $1/1^2$ or 1.

The mass of the Sun is 27,000,000 times that of the Moon and its distance from the Earth is 392 times that of the Moon. We can say, then, that the Sun is 27,000,000 Moon-masses and is at 392 Moon-distances. The gravitational pull of the Sun upon the Earth is therefore $27,000,000/392^2$ or 176. This means that the Sun's gravitational pull upon the Earth is 176 times that of the Moon. You would therefore expect the Sun to create tidal bulges on the Earth, and so it does. One bulge on the side toward itself, naturally, and one on the side opposite itself.

At the new Moon, the Moon is on the same side of the Earth as the Sun, and both Moon and Sun are pulling in the same direction. The bulges they produce separately add to each other, producing an unusually large difference between high and low tide.

At the full Moon, the Moon is on the side of the Earth opposite that of the Sun. Both, however, are producing bulges on the side nearest them *and* on the side opposite them. The Sun's near-bulge coincides with the Moon's far-bulge and vice versa. Once again, the bulges produced separately add to each other and another unusually large difference between high and low tide is produced.

Therefore the spring tides come at new Moon and full Moon.

At first and third quarter, when the Moon has the half-Moon appearance, Moon, Earth, and Sun form a right triangle. If you picture the Sun as pulling from the right and producing a tidal bulge to the right and left of the Earth, then the Moon at first quarter is pulling from above and producing a bulge up and down. (At third quarter, it is pulling from below and still producing a bulge up and down.)

In either case, the two sets of bulges tend to neutralize each other. What would ordinarily be the Moon's low tide is partially filled by the existence of the Sun's high tide, so that the range in water level between high and low tide is cut down. Thus we have the neap tides at first and third quarter.

But hold on. I said that the Moon's low tide is "partially filled" by the existence of the Sun's high tide. Only "partially." Does that mean the Sun's tidal bulges are smaller than the Moon's tidal bulges?

It sure does. The tides follow the Moon. The Sun modifies the Moon's effect but never abolishes it.

Surely, one ought to ask why that should be so. I have said that the Sun's gravitational pull on the Earth is 176 times that of the Moon. Why then should it be the Moon that produces the major tidal effect?

The answer is that it is not the gravitational pull itself that produces the tides, but the *difference* in that pull upon different parts of the Earth. The difference in gravitational pull over the Earth's width decreases rapidly as the body under consideration is moved farther off, since, as the total distance increases, the distance represented by the width of the Earth makes up a smaller and smaller part of the total.

Thus, the distance of the Sun's center from the Earth's center is about 92,900,000 miles. The Earth's width makes far less difference in this case than in the case, earlier cited, of the Moon's distance. The distance from the Sun's center to the side of the Earth near it is 92,896,000, while the distance to the far side is 92,904,000. If the distance from the Sun's center to the near side of the Earth is set equal to 1, then the distance to the far side is 1.00009. In that distance, the Sun's gravitational pull drops off to only $1/1.00009^2$ or 0.99982.

In other words, where the difference in the Moon's gravitational pull from one side of the Earth to the other is 7.0 percent; the difference of the Sun's gravitational pull is only 0.018 percent. Multiply the Sun's gravitational difference by its greater gravitational pull overall ($0.018 \times 176$) and you get 3.2 percent. The tide-producing effect of the Moon is to that of the Sun as 7.0 is to 3.2 or as 1 is to 0.46.

We see then that the Moon's effect on tides is more than twice that of the Sun, despite the Sun's much greater gravitational pull.

A second way of attaining the comparative gravitational pulls of two bodies upon the Earth is to divide their respective masses by the *cubes* of their respective distances.

Thus, since the Moon has 1 Moon-mass and is at 1 Moon-distance, its tide-producing effect is $\frac{1}{1^3}$ or 1. The Sun with 27,000,000 Moon-masses at 392 Moon-distances, has a tide-producing effect of $27,000,000/392^3$ or 0.46.

We can easily see that no body other than the Sun and the Moon can have any significant tidal effect on the Earth. The nearest sizable body other than those two is the planet Venus. It can approach as closely as 26,000,000 miles, or 108 Moon-distances, at year-and-a-half intervals. Even then its tidal effect is only $66/109^3$ or 0.0000051 times that of the Moon.

The tides, in a way, affect time. At least, it is the tides that make our day twenty-four hours long. As the tidal bulge travels about the Earth, it scrapes against shallow sea bottoms (the Bering Sea and the Irish Sea are supposed to be the prime culprits) and the energy of Earth's rotation is dissipated as frictional heat. The energy of the Earth's rotation is so huge that this dissipation represents only a very small portion of the total over any particular year or even any particular century. Still, it is enough to be slowing the Earth's rotation and lengthening the day by one second every one hundred thousand years.

This isn't much on the human time scale, but if the Earth has been in existence for five billion years and this rate of day-lengthening has been constant throughout, the day has lengthened a total of fifty thousand seconds or nearly fourteen hours. When the Earth was created, it must have been rotating on its axis in only ten hours (or less, if the tides were more important in early geologic times than they are now, as they well might have been).

As the Earth's rate of rotation slows down, it loses angular momentum as well, but this angular momentum cannot be dissipated as heat. It must be retained, as angular momentum, elsewhere in the Moon-Earth system. What the Earth loses the Moon must gain and it can do this by receding from the Earth. It's greater distance means a greater angular momentum as it turns, since angular momentum depends not only upon rate of turn, but also upon distance from the center about which an object is turning.

The effect of the tides, then, is to slow the Earth's rotation and to increase the distance of the Moon.

There is a limit to how much the Earth's rotation will be slowed. Eventually, the Earth will rotate about its axis so slowly that one side will always face the Moon as the Moon turns in its orbit. When that happens, the tidal bulges will be "frozen" into place immediately under the Moon (and on Earth's opposite side) and will no longer travel about the Earth. No more friction, no more slowing. The length of the Earth day will then be more than fifty times as long as the present day; and the more distant Moon will turn in its orbit in twice the period it now turns.

Of course, the tidal bulges of the Sun will still be moving about the Earth some seven times a year and this will have further effects on the Earth-Moon system, but never mind that now.

Even if there were no oceans on the Earth, there would still be tidal friction, for the solid substance of the Earth does yield a bit to the differential pull of the Moon. This bulge of solid material traveling around the Earth also contributes to internal friction and to the slowing of the Earth's rotation.

We can see this at work on the Moon, which has no oceans. Just as the Moon produces tides on the Earth, so the Earth produces tides on the Moon. Since the mass of the Earth is eighty-one times that of the Moon, but the distance is the same one way as the other, you might suspect that the tidal effect of Earth-on-Moon would be eighty-one times that of Moon-on-Earth. Actually, it's not quite that high. The Moon is a smaller body than the Earth so there's a smaller gravitational difference over its width than there would be in the case of the larger Earth. Without going into the details of the mathematics (after all, I must spare you something) I can give you the results—

If the effect of Moon-on-Earth is considered to be 1.00, then the effect of Earth-on-Moon is 32.5

With the Moon affected 32.5 times as much as the Earth is, and with its mass, and therefore its rotational energy, considerably less than that of the Earth, there has been ample time in the history of the solar system to dissipate its rotational energy to the point where the tidal bulge is frozen into the Moon, and where the Moon faces one side only toward the Earth. This is actually the situation.

We can suspect that any satellite which receives a tidal effect even greater than that received by the Moon would (unless it were very much larger than the Moon) also face one side to its primary at all times.

As a matter of fact, there are six other satellites in the solar system that are Moon-sized or a little larger, and each of them is attached to a planet considerably more massive than the Earth. They are therefore much more affected tidally. If we continued to consider the effect of the Moon on the Earth to be 1.00, we have Table 31:

*Table 31*

| | |
|---|---|
| Neptune-on-Triton | 720 |
| Saturn-on-Titan | 225 |
| Jupiter-on-Callisto | 225 |
| Jupiter-on-Ganymede | 945 |
| Jupiter on Europa | 145 |
| Jupiter on Io | 5,650 |

There seems no question but that all these satellites have had their rotations with respect to their primaries stopped. Each of these satellites faces one side to its primary constantly.

195

What about the reverse, though? What about the effect of the various satellites on their primaries?

Of the six Moon-sized satellites just mentioned, the two which are closest to their primaries are Io and Triton. Io is 262,000 miles from Jupiter and Triton is 219,000 miles from Neptune. Because the effect varies inversely with the cube of the distance, we can suspect that these two will have considerably more effect on their primaries than will the remaining four, which are all much farther away from their primaries.

If we consider the Jupiter/Io and Neptune/Triton pairs, then we note that Jupiter is far larger than Neptune and that there will therefore be a larger drop in the gravitational field across the width of Jupiter than across the lesser width of Neptune. Since the extent of this drop is crucial, it is fair to conclude that of the six planet/satellite combinations we have been considering, the tidal effect of Io on Jupiter is the strongest. Let's see how much that is.

Again, we are considering the tidal effect of the Moon on the Earth to be 1.00. In that case (if you will trust my calculations) the effect of Io on Jupiter is equal to 30.

This is a sizable amount, surprising to anyone who would assume, without analysis, that a small satellite like Io could scarcely have much of a gravitational effect on giant Jupiter.

Well, it has. It has thirty times the effect on Jupiter that our Moon has on the Earth. Io exerts roughly the effect on Jupiter that the Earth exerts on the Moon.

Naturally, although the Earth's effect is sufficient to stop the Moon's rotation relative to itself, we wouldn't expect Io's similar effect on Jupiter to slow Jupiter's rotation significantly. After all, Jupiter is far larger in mass than the Moon is and packs far more rotational energy into its structure. Jupiter can dissipate this rotational energy for billions of years without slowing its rotation much while the Moon, dissipating its rotational energy at the same rate is brought to a halt. And, indeed, Jupiter still rotates with a period of only ten hours.

However, there are tidal effects other than rotation-slowing. It has recently been discovered that Jupiter's emission of radio waves varies in time with the rotation of Io. This seems to puzzle astronomers and a number of theories to explain it have been proposed which I am not sure I exactly understand. (I am not, after all, a professional astronomer.)

I suspect that these explanations must surely take into account Io's tidal action on Jupiter's huge atmosphere. This tidal action must affect the turbulence of that atmosphere and therefore its radio emission. In the extremely unlikely case that this has not been considered, I offer the suggestion to all comers free of charge.

That leaves only one more thing to consider. I have discussed the effect of the Sun upon Earth's tides. This is not terribly large (0.46) and one can expect that since the Sun's tide-producing effect drops off as the cube of the distance, the effect on planets more distant than the Earth would prove to be insignificant.

What about the effect on Venus and Mercury, however, which are closer to the Sun than is the Earth?

Well, according to my calculations, the Sun's tidal effect on Venus is 1.06 and its effect on Mercury is 3.77.

These are intermediate figures. They are more than the Moon's effect on Earth, which is not sufficient to stop Earth's rotation altogether; but they are less than the Earth's effect on the Moon, which was enough to stop the Moon.

One might suppose, then, that the rotations of Venus and Mercury, while slowed, would not yet have slowed to a stop.

Nevertheless, for a long time, the rotations of Venus

and Mercury *were* considered as having been stopped, so that both planets faced a single side to the Sun at all times. In the case of Venus, this was a pure guess, for no one had ever seen the surface, but the case of Mercury, where surface markings could be made out (though obscurely) the feeling seemed to check with observations.

In the last year or two, however, this view has had to be revised in the case of both planets. Venus and Mercury are each rotating slowly with respect to the Sun as (with the wisdom of hindsight) one might have suspected from the figures on tidal effects.

# 14. THE ROCKS OF DAMOCLES

IN SOME WAYS, science fiction writers aren't doing too well these days. In late 1962, Mariner II seemed to settle the question of the surface temperature of Venus, placing it far above the boiling point of water.

With that, there vanished some of the most beautiful settings for s.f. stories. Old-timers may remember with nostalgia, as I do, the moist, swampy world of Weinbaum's "Parasite Planet." Well, it's gone! For that matter, I wrote a short novel under a pseudonym, only ten years ago, that was set on a Venus that was one huge ocean, with Earth-cities built underwater in the shallower regions. . . . All gone!

Now along comes Mariner IV and discovers craters (but no canals) on Mars.

No one expected that! I don't know of a single science fiction story that had ever placed craters on Mars. . . . Canals, yes, but craters, no! I have written several stories set on Mars and I have always mentioned the canals (I placed no water in them; I knew enough for that) but I've never had craters.

And yet, going by the photographs sent back by Mariner IV, the Martian surface is some four times as rich in craters as the Moon is.

Fortunately for science-fictional self-respect, astronomers themselves didn't do much better. Not one of them, as far as I know, suggested Venus might be as hot as Mercury until after the first microwave observations came to be analyzed in detail. And very few even speculated on the possibility of a cratered Mars.

In the first flush of the Martian pictures, the newspapers announced that this meant there was no life on Mars. To be sure, the pictures didn't give us life-enthusiasts anything to cheer about but, as it turns out, things aren't all that bad.

The mere fact that the pictures show no signs of life means nothing in itself, of course. Some of our own weather satellites have taken numerous pictures of the Earth under conditions comparable to those of Mariner IV and Mars, and the Earth pictures show no signs of life on our planet, either. I don't mean no signs of man; I mean no signs of any life at all. And, mind you, we know where to look for signs of life on Earth, and what to look for.

A more subtle argument for the anti-life view rests upon the mere existence of all those craters on Mars. If Mars had ever had an ample ocean and atmosphere those craters would have been eroded away. Since the craters are there, goes the argument, Mars has always been desiccated and almost airless and, therefore, the chances of life having developed in the first place are extremely small.

Quickly, however, the pro-life forces shot back. Since Mars is much closer to the asteroid zone than the Moon is, and since the asteroids are very likely to be the source of the large bodies that collide with planets and form sizable craters, Mars ought to have something like twenty-five times as many craters per unit surface area as the Moon does. It appears to have only four times as many; only one-sixth the expected number. What happened to the other five-sixths?

Eroded away!

If so, then the craters we do see represent the youngest sixth, the ones that have not had time to erode away yet. Assuming that the process of erosion proceeds at uniform speed, then the marks we see only tell us about the last sixth of Martian history—say six to seven hundred million years.

What happened before that we still can't tell. Water may have been present in larger quantities before then and life might have started on a comparatively water-rich and water-comfortable Mars. If so, Martian life may have been hardly enough to survive even now on the gradually bleaching bones of the planet.

Maybe not, but we can't tell from only the pictures we have. We will need much more detailed photographs or, better yet, a manned expedition to Mars.

Still, craters on Mars do set one thinking. In the course of the history of the solar system (its inner regions, at least) the major worlds must have undergone a continuous peppering bombardment from smaller bodies. The Moon and Mars bear the visible scars of this and it is quite out of the question to suppose that the Earth could possibly have escaped its share of the bombardment.

Although the Earth is as far from the asteroid zone as the Moon is, it is eighty-one times as massive as the Moon and, at equivalent distances, pulls with eighty-one times the force. Furthermore, Earth is the larger target, with fourteen times the cross-sectional area of the Moon, so it should have endured many times as many collisions. In fact, although Earth is much farther from the asteroid zone than Mars is, it has 3.5 times the cross-sectional area and ten times the mass of Mars, and I suspect it has suffered more of a peppering than Mars has.

The Moon is supposed to have 300,000 craters with diameters of one kilometer or more. Even allowing for the fact that the Earth is seventy percent ocean, which can absorb collisions without being marked up as a result, the remaining thirty percent—Earth's land surface—might well have suffered at least a million collisions in its billions of years of history.

Where are they all? Erased! The effect of wind, water, and living things quickly wipes them out and every last trace of more than ninety-nine percent of the craters formed on Earth must have vanished by now.

But surely there are remnants of the more recent ones. All one need do is look for depressions in the Earth that are more or less circular. These are easy to find, as a matter of fact, especially since they need only be roughly circular. After all, unevennesses can be put down to the effects of erosion, slippage, further bombardment, and so on.

A nice near-circular depression might fill with water and form a near-circular sea. The Aral Sea is an example. Then, too, the northern boundary of the Black Sea forms a near-circular arc. The Gulf of Mexico can almost be made to fit a semicircle. For that matter the Indian Ocean, and even the Pacific Ocean, have coastlines that can be made to fit circles with surprising closeness.

Whether you find such circles or not depends on how eagerly you want to find them and how ready you are to dismiss departure from strict circularity.

One of those most eager to find possible craters is Dr. Frank Dachille of Pennsylvania State University. At least, the university has just sent me a discussion of his views, which includes a map on which no less than forty-two "probable and putative" meteorite craters or groups of craters are listed in the United States and near-vicinity alone.

Of these, the largest in the United States proper is what is marked down as the "Michigan Basin." This is the near-circle formed by Lakes Michigan and Huron, a circle some three hundred miles in diameter. According to Dachille's estimate a crater this large would have to be caused by a meteorite thirty or forty miles in diameter.

On the map a still larger crater is indicated as "Kelly Crater," and this marks out the Atlantic coastline of the United States along the continental shelf. This forms an arc of about one-third of a circle which would be over twelve hundred miles in diameter if it were complete. I suppose that would require a meteorite a hundred miles in diameter or so—in other words, one of the larger asteroids.

One might dismiss such catastrophic events as having been confined to a highly specialized period of planetary history. At the very beginning of the formation of the solar system, planetesimals were gathering together to form the planets and the last few really large ones could have left the huge scars that mark the oceans on the Earth and the "seas" on the Moon.

Or else there was a period in planetary history during which a possible planet between Mars and Jupiter exploded (or underwent a series of explosions) leaving the asteroid belt behind and riddling the solar system from Mercury to Jupiter with flying shrapnel in bits up to a hundred miles across.

In either case, one might argue, this specialized period is over, the damage is done, the craters are formed, and we can dismiss the matter. There are no more planet-busters, no more asteroids of one hundred miles in diameter or more floating around within reaching distance of the Earth.

Indeed, that is so. There is no body that ever approaches within 25 million miles of the Earth that is over, let us say, twenty-five miles in diameter, except for the Moon itself, and there is no reason to expect the Moon to leave its orbit. Are we safe, then?

No, we are not! Space is loaded with dust particles and pebbles that burst into our atmosphere, glow, and vaporize harmlessly. In addition, however, larger chunks—not large enough to gouge out an ocean, perhaps, but large enough to do horrendous damage—are moving near us.

We can after all find craters that are indubitably craters and that are in such good condition that they must be quite new. The most spectacular of these craters is located near Winslow, Arizona. It looks just like a small lunar crater; it is roughly circular, with an average diameter of about 4,150 feet or four-fifths of a mile. It is 570 feet deep and the bottom is filled with a layer of mashed and broken debris about 600 feet thick. It is surrounded by a wall which is from 130 to 160 feet higher than the surrounding plain.

The first to demonstrate that the crater was caused by a meteorite (and was not an extinct volcano) was the American mining engineer Daniel Moreau Barringer, and the site is therefore called the Barringer Crater. Because of its origin it also bears the more dramatic name Meteor Crater. I have even seen it called the Great Barringer Meteor Crater, a name which honors, at one stroke, the size, the man, and the origin.

The fact that the strike took place in an arid region where the effects of water and living things are minimal has kept the Barringer Crater in better preservation than would have been the case if it were located in most places on Earth. Even so, its condition is such that it is not likely to be more than fifty thousand years old and, geologically speaking, that is yesterday.

If the meteorite that formed it (some millions of tons in mass) had struck now, and in the proper spot, it could, at one stroke, wipe out the largest city on Earth, and more or less destroy vast tracts of its suburbs.

Other strikes (not as large to be sure) have taken place even in historic times, two respectable ones in the twentieth century. One took place in northern Siberia in 1908. It involved a meteor of only a few dozen tons of mass, perhaps, but that was enough to gouge out craters up to one hundred and fifty feet in diameter and to knock down trees for twenty to thirty miles around.

That will do, and how! A fall like that in the middle of Manhattan would probably knock down every building on the island and large numbers across the rivers on either side, killing several million people within minutes of impact.

In fact, that 1908 fall did come close to wiping out a major city. It has been calculated that if the meteor had moved in an orbit parallel to its actual path, but had been displaced just enough in space to allow the Earth to rotate for five more hours before impact, it would have hit St. Petersburg (then the capital of the Russian Empire and now Leningrad) right on the nose.

Then, in 1947, there was another such fall, but a smaller one, in far-eastern Siberia.

Two falls, then, both in Siberia, and both doing virtually no damage except to trees and wild animals. Mankind has clearly had an unusual run of luck.

There are some astronomers who estimate that there may be two such "city-busters" hitting Earth per century. If so, we can make some calculations. The area of the city of New York is about $1/670,000$ of the Earth's surface. If we assume that a city-buster can strike any place on Earth, at random, then a given city-buster has 1 chance in 670,000 of hitting New York.

If it comes, on the average, once every fifty years, then its chances of hitting New York in any one particular year is 1 in 670,000 times 50, or 1 in 33,000,000.

But New York is only one city out of many. If we consider that the total densely urbanized area on Earth is 330 times the area of New York (my spur-of-the-moment estimate) then the chance of some urban center being flattened by a city-buster in any given year is 1 in 100,000.

To put it another way, it's even money that sometime within the next hundred thousand years, some good-sized city somewhere on Earth will be wiped out by a city-buster. And that is probably an overoptimistic prediction since the urbanized area on Earth is increasing and may continue to increase for quite a while, presenting a much better target.

This makes it clear, too, why no urbanized area in the past has been destroyed. Cities have only existed for say seven thousand years and until the last couple of centuries, the really large ones have been few and widely scattered. The chances for a major disaster of this sort having taken place at any time in recorded history is probably not better than 1 in 100—and it hasn't happened.

But must we have a direct hit? What about the dangers of a near-miss. On land, a near-miss may be tolerable. Even a 1908-type meteorite striking land fifty miles from a populated center may leave that center intact. But what if the meteorite strikes the ocean? Three out of four, after all, ought to.

If the meteorite is not inordinately large and if it strikes far enough away from a coastline, the damage may be small. But there is always a chance that a large meteorite may strike near a coastline, even perhaps in a landlocked arm of the sea. It might then do severe damage, and since the appropriate regions of the sea are much larger in area than are the cities of the world, the chances of a catastrophic oceanic near-miss are correspondingly greater than the chances of a dead-center hit on a city.

The oceanic near-miss might be expected, on the average, not once in a hundred thousand years, but once in ten thousand years or even less. In short, there should be some record of such disasters in historical times, and I think that perhaps there are.

Noah's Flood *did* happen. Or, put it this way— There was a vast and disastrous flood in the Tigris-Euphrates some six thousand years ago. Concerning this, Babylonian stories were handed down which, with the generations, were interlarded with mythological detail.

The tale of Noah's Flood as given in the Bible is a version of those stories.

Nor is this speculation. Archaeological probings on the sites of some of the ancient cities of Babylonia have come across thick layers of sediment within which there are no human remains or artifacts.

What laid down these sediments? The usual suggestion is that since the Tigris-Euphrates complex floods occasionally, it may have flooded particularly disastrously on one occasion. This has always seemed insufficient to me. I don't see how any river flood can possibly lay down all the observed sediment or do the kind of damage dramatized later in the tales of universal flood, death, and destruction—even allowing for the natural exaggeration of storytellers.

I have an alternative suggestion which, as far as I know, is original with me. I have seen nothing about it anywhere.

What if a city-buster meteorite had, some six thousand years ago, landed in the Persian Gulf. The Persian Gulf is nearly landlocked and such an impact might well have heaved up a wall of water that would move northwestward and would burst in, with absolutely devastating impact, upon the low plain of the Tigris-Euphrates valley.

It would be a super-tsunami, a tidal wave to end all tidal waves, and it would scour much of the valley clean. The water would cover what was indeed "all the world" to the inhabitants and drown countless numbers in its path.

In support of this notion, I would like to point out that the Bible speaks of more than rain. Genesis 7:11 says not only that "the windows of heaven were opened" meaning that it rained, but also that "the same day were all the fountains of the great deep broken up." Meaning what? Meaning, it seems to me, that the water came in from the sea.

Furthermore, Noah's ark lacked any motive power,

207

either sails or oars, and simply drifted. Where did it drift? It came to rest on the mountains of Ararat (the ancient Urartu) in the Caucasian foothills northwest of the Tigris-Euphrates. But an ordinary river flood would have washed boats southeastward out to sea. Only a tidal wave of unprecedented scope would have carried the ark northwestward.

Nor need Noah's Flood be the only tale of a remembered oceanic near-miss. Many peoples (but not all) have flood legends, and it may have been such a flood legend that gave rise to the dim tales that Plato finally dramatized in his story of Atlantic. Such catastrophes may indeed have happened more than once in the memory of man.

When will the next disaster come? A hundred thousand years hence? A thousand years? Tomorrow? There's no way of telling.

Of course, we might scan near-space and see what's floating around there.

Till 1898, the answer was Nothing! Between the orbits of Mars and Venus was nothing of any consequence save the Earth and Moon, for all anyone could tell. Nothing worse than pebbles and small boulders, at any rate, that could produce the effect of a shooting star and occasionally reach Earth's surface. A meteorite might conceivably kill a man or demolish a house, but the damage to be expected of meteorites was only the tiniest fraction of that done by lightning bolts, for instance, and man has managed to live with the thunderstorm.

Then in 1898, the German astronomer Gustav Witt discovered Asteroid 433. Nothing unusual, until Witt calculated its orbit. This was elliptical, of course, and in that part of the elliptical path that was farthest from the Sun, the asteroid traveled between Mars and Jupiter as did all asteroids till then discovered.

In the remainder of its orbit, however, it traveled between the orbits of Mars and Earth. Its orbit approached within 14 million miles of that of Earth and at set intervals, when both objects were at just the right place in their respective orbits, that approach would be realized and the asteroid would be at only half the distance from us that Venus is. Witt named the asteroid Eros after the son of Mars and Venus in the classical myths. That began the practice of masculine names for all asteroids with unusual orbits.

Eros's close approach was a matter of self-congratulation among scientists. It could be used to determine the dimensions of the solar system with unprecedented accuracy, when close. And this was done in 1931, when it approached within 17 million miles. From the periodic flickering of its light, it was decided that Eros was not a sphere but an irregular, roughly brick-shaped object which brightened when we saw it long-ways and dimmed when we saw it end-ways. Its longest diameter is estimated to be fifteen miles and its shortest five miles.

There was no particular nervousness felt about Eros's close approach. After all, 14 million miles isn't exactly *close*, you know.

As time went on, however, several additional objects were discovered with orbits that came closer to Earth's than that of Venus does, and such objects came to be called "Earth-grazers." Several of them passed closer to the Sun than Venus does and one of them, Icarus, actually moves in closer to the Sun than Mercury does.

The climax came in 1937, when the asteroid Hermes was discovered by an astronomer named Reinmuth. On October 30, it passed within 487,000 miles of the Earth and the calculation of its orbit seems to show that it might possibly come within 200,000 miles—closer than the Moon! (For information on some Earth-grazers, *see* Table 32.)

*Table 32*

THE EARTH-GRAZERS

| NAME | YEAR OF DISCOVERY | LENGTH OF ORBITAL PERIOD (YEARS) | ESTIMATED MAXIMUM DIAMETER (MILES) | ESTIMATED MASS (TRILLIONS OF TONS) | CLOSEST APPROACH TO EARTH (MILLIONS OF MILES) |
|---|---|---|---|---|---|
| Albert | 1911 | c. 4 | 3 | 300 | 20 |
| Eros | 1898 | 1.76 | 15 | 15,000 | 14 |
| Amor | 1932 | 2.67 | 10 | 12,000 | 10 |
| Apollo | 1932 | 1.81 | 2 | 100 | 7 |
| Icarus | 1949 | 1.12 | 1 | 12 | 4 |
| Adonis | 1936 | 2.76 | 1 | 12 | 1.5 |
| Hermes | 1937 | 1.47 | 1 | 12 | 0.2 |

Even so, why worry? A miss of two hundred thousand miles is still a fair-sized miss, isn't it?

No, it isn't, and for three reasons. In the first place, the orbits of asteroids aren't necessarily fixed. The Earth-grazers have small masses, astronomically speaking, and a close approach to a larger world can introduce changes in that orbit. Comets, for instance, which have asteroidal masses, have been observed on more than one occasion to undergo radical orbital changes as a result of close approaches to Jupiter. Hermes doesn't approach Jupiter at all closely to be sure, but it does skim the Earth-Moon system, and, on occasion. Mercury, and it is subject to orbital change for that reason.

As a matter of fact, Hermes hasn't been located since its first sighting in 1937, though it should have come fairly close every three years or so. This may well mean that its orbit has already changed somewhat so that we don't know the right place to look for it and will rediscover it, if at all, only by accident.

A random change in Hermes' orbit is much more likely to move it away from Earth than toward it, since there is much more room away than toward. Still, there is a finite chance that such a change might cause it to zero in, and a direct collision of Hermes and Earth is horrifying to think of. The Earth won't be perceptibly damaged, but we could be. If you think that a meteorite a few million tons in mass could gouge out a hole nearly a mile across, you can see that Hermes, with a few trillions of tons of mass, could excavate a good-sized portion of an American state or a European nation.

Secondly, these Earth-grazers probably haven't been in their orbit through all the history of the solar system. Some collision, some perturbation, has shifted their orbits—originally within the asteroid belt—and caused them to fall in toward the Sun. On occasion, then, new ones might join them. Naturally, it is the smaller asteroids that stand the best chance of serious orbital changes but there are thousands of Hermes-sized asteroids in the asteroid belt and Earth can still witness the coming of unwelcome new strangers.

Thirdly, the only Earth-grazers we can detect are those big enough to see at hundreds of thousands of miles. There are bound to be smaller ones in greater profusion. If there are half a dozen objects a mile in diameter and more that come wandering into near-space on occasion, there may be half a thousand or more which are one hundred feet in diameter or so, and which could still do tremendous damage if they wandered in too closely.

No, I see no way, at present, of either predicting or avoiding the occurrence of a very occasional major catastrophe. We spin through space with the possibility of collision with these Rocks of Damocles ever present.

In the future, perhaps, things may be different. The men in the space stations that will eventually be set up about the Earth may find themselves, among other things, on the watch for the Earth-grazers, something like the iceberg watch conducted in northern waters since the sinking of the Titanic (but much more difficult of course).

The rocks, boulders, and mountains of space may be painstakingly tagged and numbered. Their changing orbits may be kept under steady watch. Then, a hundred years from now, perhaps, or a thousand, some computer on such a station will sound the alarm: "Collision orbit!"

Then a counterattack, kept in waiting for all that time would be set in motion. The dangerous rock would be met with an H-bomb (or, by that time, something more appropriate) designed to trigger off on collision. The rock would glow and vaporize and change from a boulder to a conglomeration of pebbles.

Even if they continued on course, the threat would be lifted. Earth would merely be treated to a spectacular (and harmless) shower of shooting stars.

Until then, however, the Rocks of Damocles remain suspended, and eternity for millions of us may, at any time, be an hour away.

# 15. HARMONY IN HEAVEN

I NEVER ACTUALLY took any courses in astronomy, which is something I regret for, looking back on it now, there were a number of courses I did take which I might cheerfully have sacrificed for a bit of astronomy.

However, one must look at the bright side, which is that now, every once in a while, I come across a little item in my astronomical reading which gladdens my heart by teaching me something new. If I had had formal training in the field, then these items would all have been old stuff and I would have missed my moments of delight.

For instance, I have come across a recent text in astronomy, *Introduction to Astronomy* by Dean B. McLaughlin (Houghton Mifflin, 1961) which has delighted me in this fashion in several places. Let me, therefore, recommend it to all of you without reservation.

As an example, Professor McLaughlin intrigued me so much with his comments on Kepler's harmonic law that, in my ecstasy, I devoted more thought to it than I had ever done before, and I see no reason why I should not share the results of that thinking with you. In fact, I insist upon it.

I might begin, I suppose, by answering the question that I know is in all your minds: What is Kepler's harmonic law? Well—

In 1619, the German astronomer, Johannes Kepler, discovered a neat relationship between the relative distances of the planets from the Sun, and their periods of revolution about the Sun.

Now for two thousand years, philosophers had felt that planets were spaced at such distances that their movements gave rise to sounds that united in heavenly harmony (the "music of the spheres"). This was in analogy to the manner in which strings of certain different lengths gave forth sound that united in pleasing harmony when simultaneously struck.

For that reason, Kepler's relationship of distances and periods, which is usually called, with scientific dullness, "Kepler's third law" (since he had earlier discovered two other important generalizations about planetary orbits) is also called, much more romantically, "Kepler's harmonic law."

The law may be stated thus: "The squares of the periods of the planets are proportional to the cubes of their mean distances from the Sun."

To follow up the consequences of this, let's get slightly mathematical (as slightly as possible, I promise). Let's begin by considering two planets of the solar system, planet-1 and planet-2. Planet-1 is at mean distance $D_1$ from the Sun and planet-2 is at mean distance $D_2$ ("Mean" means "average.") Their periods of revolution are, respectively, $P_1$ and $P_2$. Then, by Kepler's harmonic law, we can say that:

$$P_1{}^2/P_2{}^2 = D_1{}^3/D_2{}^3 \qquad \text{(Equation 10)}$$

This is not a very complicated equation, but any equation that can be simplified *should* be simplified, and that's what I'm going to do next. Let's pretend that planet-2 is the Earth and that we are going to measure all periods of revolution in years and all distances in astronomical units (A.U.).

The period of revolution of the Earth, by definition, is one year; therefore $P_2$ and $P_2{}^2$ both equal 1. Then, too,

214

the astronomical unit is defined as the mean distance of the Earth from the Sun. Consequently, the Earth is 1 A.U. from the Sun, which means that $D_2$ and $D_2{}^3$ both equal 1.

The denominators of both fractions in Equation 10 become unity and disappear. With only one set of Ps and Ds to worry about, we can eliminate subscripts and write Equation 10 simply as follows:

$$P^2 = D^3 \qquad \text{(Equation 11)}$$

provided we remember to express P in years and D in astronomical units.

Just to show how this works let's consider the nine major planets of the solar system, and list for each the period of revolution in years and the distance from the Sun in astronomical units (see Table 33). If, for each planet, you take the square of the value under P and the

*Table 33*

| PLANET | P (PERIOD OF REVOLUTION IN YEARS) | D (MEAN DISTANCE IN A.U.) |
|---|---|---|
| Mercury | 0.241 | 0.387 |
| Venus | 0.615 | 0.723 |
| Earth | 1.000 | 1.000 |
| Mars | 1.881 | 1.524 |
| Jupiter | 11.86 | 5.203 |
| Saturn | 29.46 | 9.54 |
| Uranus | 84.01 | 19.18 |
| Neptune | 164.8 | 30.06 |
| Pluto | 248.4 | 39.52 |

cube of the value under D you will find, indeed, that the two results are virtually identical.

Of course, the period and distance of any given planet can be determined separately and independently by actual observation. The connection between the two, therefore, is interesting but not vital. However, what if we can't determine both quantities independently. Suppose, for instance, you imagined a planet between Mars and Jupiter at a distance of just 4 A.U. from the Sun. What would its period of revolution be? Or if you imagined a far, far distant planet, 6,000 A.U. from the Sun. What would *its* period of revolution be?

From Equation 11, we see that:

$$P = \sqrt{D^3} \qquad \text{(Equation 12)}$$

and therefore we can answer the questions easily. In the case of the planet between Mars and Jupiter, the period of revolution would be the square root of the cube of four, or just eight years. As for the far distant planet, its period would be the square root of the cube of 6,000 and that comes to 465,000 years.

You can work it the other way round, too, by converting Equation 11 into:

$$D = \sqrt[3]{P^2} \qquad \text{(Equation 13)}$$

You can then find out how distant from the Sun a planet must be to have a period of revolution of just twenty years, or just one million years.

In the former case, you must take the cube root of the square of twenty and in the latter, the cube root of the square of one million. This gives you an answer of 7.35 A.U. for the first case and about 10,000 A.U. for the second.

We can have a little fun, now, by seeking extremes.* For instance, how far out can a planet be and still be a member of the solar system? The nearest star system to ourselves is Alpha Centauri, which is 4.3 light-years away. Any planet which is as close as 2 light-years to the Sun must therefore be closer to the Sun than to any other star no matter what the plane of its orbit. It is safely in the Sun's grip and let's consider it the "farthest reasonable planet."

*In theory only, let me firmly state, lest my politics be misconstrued.

An astronomical unit is equal to about 93,000,000 miles while a light-year is equal to about 5,860,000,000,000 miles. Therefore, one light-year is equal to about 63,000 A.U. and our farthest reasonable planet is at a distance of about 126,000 A.U. From Equation 12, then, we can see that the period of the farthest reasonable planet is about 45,000,000 years.

Let's ask next, how close a planet can be to the Sun? Let's ignore temperature and gas resistance and suppose that a planet can circle the Sun at its equator, just skimming its surface. We can call this a "surface planet."

The distance of a planet from the Sun is always measured center to center. If we consider the surface planet to be of negligible size, then its distance from the Sun is equal to the radius of the Sun, which is 432,300 miles or 0.00465 A.U. Again using Equation 12, we can show that the period of such a body is 0.00031 years or 2.73 hours.

Next let's find out how fast a planet is moving, on the average, in miles per second (relative to the Sun). To do so, let's first figure out how many seconds it takes the planet to make a complete turn in its orbit. We already have that period in years (P). In each year, there are about 31,557,000 seconds. Therefore the period of the planet in seconds is 31,557,000 P.

An astronomical unit is, as I said before, about 93,000,000 miles. We have the distance of a planet in astronomical units (D), so that the distance in miles is 93,000,000 D. What we really need at this point, however is the length of the orbit itself. If we assume the orbit to be an exact circle (which is approximately true) then its length is equal to its distance from the Sun, multiplied by twice "pi." The value of "pi" is 3.1416 and twice that is 6.2832. If we multiply that by the distance of the planet in miles, we get the length of the planetary orbit in miles, and that is 584,000,000 D.

To find the average velocity of a planet in miles per

second, we must divide the length of the orbit in miles (584,000,000 D) by the duration of its period of revolution in seconds (31,557,000 P). This gives us the value 18.5 D/P, for the mean orbital velocity of a planet.

We can simplify this by remembering that $P=\sqrt{D^3}$, according to Equation 12, so that we can write the velocity of a moving planet as $18.5 \ D/\sqrt{D^3}$. Since $\sqrt{D^3}$ is equal to $\sqrt{D^2} \times D$, or $D\sqrt{D}$, we can write the velocity of a planet in orbit as equal to $18.5 \ D/D\sqrt{D}$ or, in a final simplification, letting V stand for velocity:

$$V = 18.5/\sqrt{D} \qquad \text{(Equation 14)}$$

Remember that D represents the distance of a planet from the Sun in astronomical units. For the Earth the value of D is equal to 1 and the square root of D is also equal to 1. Therefore, the Earth moves in its orbit at the average rate of 18.5 miles per second.

Since D is known for the other planets, the mean orbital velocity can be calculated without trouble by taking the square root of D and dividing it into 18.5. The result is Table 34:

*Table 34*

| PLANET | MEAN ORBITAL VELOCITY (MILES PER SECOND) |
|---|---|
| Mercury | 29.8 |
| Venus | 21.7 |
| Earth | 18.5 |
| Mars | 15.0 |
| Jupiter | 8.2 |
| Saturn | 6.0 |
| Uranus | 4.2 |
| Neptune | 3.4 |
| Pluto | 2.9 |

Nowadays, velocity is often spoken of in "Mach numbers," where Mach 1 is equivalent to the speed of sound in air, Mach 2 to twice that speed, and so on. at 0°C the speed of sound is 1,090 feet per second, or just about 0.2 miles per second. Our fastest airplanes are now moving along at Mach 2 and more, while an astronaut in orbit moves at about Mach 25 with respect to the Earth.

Compare this with Pluto, which moves (with respect to the Sun) at a mere Mach 14.5, only half the velocity of an astronaut. The Earth on the other hand is moving at a respectable Mach 93 and Mercury at a zippy Mach 149.

But let's try our extremes again.

The farthest reasonable planet, at 126,000 A.U., would have an orbital velocity of just about 0.052 miles per second, or about Mach 0.26. It's rather impressive that even at a distance of two light-years, the Sun is still capable of lashing a planet into traveling at one-quarter the speed of sound.

As for the surface planet at a distance of 0.00465 A.U., its orbital velocity must be 271 miles per second, or Mach 1,3555. (Incidentally, the fastest conceivable velocity, that of light in a vacuum, is equal to about Mach 930,000, so watch out for anyone who talks casually about Mach 1,000,000. Bet him you can't reach Mach 1,000,000 and you'll win.)

Actually, a planet orbits about the Sun not in a circle but in an ellipse with the Sun at one focus (Kepler's first law). If you imagine a line connecting the Sun and the planet (a "radius vector"), that line would sweep out equal areas in equal times. (This is Kepler's second law.) When the planet is close to the Sun, the radius vector is short and, to sweep out a given area, it must move through a comparatively large angle. When the planet is far from the Sun, the radius vector is long and, to sweep out the same area, needs to move through a smaller angle.

Thus, Kepler's second law describes the manner in which a planet's orbital velocity speeds up as it approaches the Sun and slows down as it recedes from it. I would like to point out one consequence of this without going into mathematical detail.

Imagine a planet suddenly increasing its velocity at some point in its orbit. The effect upon it would be analogous to that of throwing it away from the Sun. It would move away from the Sun at a steadily decreasing velocity, come to a halt, and then start falling toward the Sun again.

This resembles the situation where one throws a stone into the air here on Earth, but since the planet is also revolving about the Sun, the effect is not a simple up-and-down motion, as it is in the case of the stone.

Instead, the planet revolves as it recedes from the Sun, its orbital velocity decreasing until it reaches a point that is precisely on the other side of the Sun from the point at which its velocity had suddenly increased. At this point on the other side of the Sun, its distance from the Sun has increased to a maximum (aphelion), and its orbital velocity has slowed to a minimum.

As the planet continues past the aphelion, it begins to approach the Sun again and its orbital velocity increases once more. When it returns to the place at which it had suddenly increased its velocity, it would be at that point in its new orbit which was nearest the Sun (perihelion) and its orbital velocity would then be at a maximum.

The greater the velocity at a given perihelion distance, the more distant the aphelion and the more elongated the elliptical orbit. The elongation increases at a greater and greater rate with equal increments of speed because as the aphelion recedes, the strength of the Sun's gravity weakens and it can do less and less to prevent a still further recession.

Eventually, at some particular velocity at a given perihelion distance, the ellipse elongates to infinity—that is, it becomes a parabola. The planet continues along the parabolic orbit, receding from the Sun forever and never returning. This velocity is the "escape velocity" and it can be determined for any given planet by multiplying the mean orbital velocity in Table 34 by the square root of two; that is, by 1.414. The result is shown in Table 35.

Thus, if the Earth, for any reason, ever moved at 26.2 miles per second or more, it would leave the solar system forever. (However, don't lose sleep over this. There is nothing, short of the invasion of another star, that can bring this about.)

Escape velocity for the farthest reasonable planet would be 0.073 miles per second while that for the surface planet would be 385 miles per second.

*Table 35*

| PLANET | ESCAPE VELOCITY (MILES PER SECOND) |
|---|---|
| Mercury | 42.1 |
| Venus | 30.7 |
| Earth | 26.2 |
| Mars | 21.2 |
| Jupiter | 11.6 |
| Saturn | 8.5 |
| Uranus | 5.9 |
| Neptune | 4.8 |
| Pluto | 4.1 |

Isaac Newton used Kepler's three laws as a guide in the working out of his own theory of gravitation. Once gravitation was worked out, Newton showed that Kepler's three laws could be deduced from it. In fact, he showed that Kepler's harmonic law as originally stated (*see* Equation 10) was only an approximation. In order to make it really exact, the masses of the Sun and the planets had to be taken into account. Equation 10 would have to be written in this way:

$$(M+m_1)P_1^2/(M+m_2)P_2^2 = D_1^3/D_2^3 \quad \text{(Equation 15)}$$

where, as before, $P_1$ and $P_2$ are the periods of revolution of planet-1 and planet-2, $D_1$ and $D_2$ are their respective distances, and where the new symbols $m_1$ and $m_2$ are their respective masses. The symbol M represents the mass of the Sun.

As it happens, the mass of the Sun is overwhelmingly greater than the mass of any of the planets. Even the largest planet, Jupiter, has only $\frac{1}{1000}$ the mass of the Sun. Consequently, the sum of M and $m_1$ or of M and $m_2$ can be taken, without significant inaccuracy, to be equal to M itself. Equation 15 can therefore be written as follows:

$$MP_1^2/MP_2^2 = D_1^3/D_2^3 \qquad \text{(Equation 16)}$$

The M's cancel and we have Equation 10.

Of course, you may decide that since Newton's correct form works out to be just about exactly that of Kepler's approximate form, why not stick with Kepler, who is simpler?

Ah, but Newton's form can be applied more broadly.

Jupiter's satellites had been discovered nine years before Kepler had announced his harmonic law. Kepler had worked out that law entirely from the planets, yet when he studied Jupiter's satellite system, he found it applied to that, too.

Newton was able to show from his theory of gravitation that all three of Kepler's laws would apply to any system of bodies moving about some central body and his form of the harmonic law could be applied to two or more different systems at once.

Suppose, for instance, that planet-1 is circling Sun-1 and planet-2 is circling Sun-2. You can say that:

$$(M_1+m_1)P_1^2/(M_2+m_2)P_2^2 = D_1^3/D_2^3 \qquad \text{(Equation 17)}$$

where $M_1$ and $M_2$ are the masses of Sun-1 and Sun-2 where $m_1$, $P_1$, and $D_1$ are the mass, period, and distance of planet-1, and where $m_2$, $P_2$, and $D_2$ are the mass, period and distance of planet-2.

Now let's simplify that rather formidable assemblage of symbols. In the first place, we can take it for granted that the planet is always so much smaller than the Sun that its mass can be neglected. (This is not always true but it's true in the solar system.) In other words, we can eliminate $m_1$ and $m_2$ and write Equation 17 as:

$$M_1P_1^2/M_2P_2^2 = D_1^3/D_2^3 \qquad \text{(Equation 18)}$$

Secondly, let's take the situation of the Earth revolving about the Sun as the norm and consider it to be the planet-2/Sun-2 system. We will measure all distances in astronomical units so that $D_2^3$ will equal 1. We will measure all periods of revolution in years so that $P_2^2$ will equal 1. Also we will measure the mass of all Suns in terms of the mass of our own Sun taken as 1. That means that $M_2$, the mass of the Sun, is equal to 1. Equation 18 becomes (dropping all subscripts)

$$MP^2 = D^3 \qquad \text{(Equation 19)}$$

where the symbols refer to the system other than the Earth/Sun system.

Suppose, for instance, that for the other Sun, we chose the Earth itself. (The Earth can serve as a central body around which smaller bodies, satellites, can revolve.) Suppose, further, that we wanted to calculate the period of revolution of a body circling the Earth at a mean distance of 237,000 miles. Since it is a period of revolution we are seeking, let us rewrite Equation 19 as:

$$P = \sqrt{D^3/M} \qquad \text{(Equation 20)}$$

The value of D is equal to 237,000 miles or 0.00255 A.U. The value of M is equal to the mass of the Earth expressed in Sun-masses. The Earth's mass is $\frac{1}{332,500}$ of the Sun or 0.000003 Sun-masses. Substituting these values into Equation 20, we find that P, the period of revolution, comes out to 0.0745 years, or 27.3 days.

It happens that the Moon is at an average distance of 237,000 miles from the Earth, and it happens that its period of revolution (relative to the stars) is 27.3 days. Consequently, Kepler's harmonic law, as corrected by Newton, applies as much to the Earth-Moon system as to the Sun-planet system.

Furthermore, since the distance of the Moon from the Earth and the Moon's period of revolution are both known; and since the distance of the Earth from the Sun and the Earth's period of revolution are also both known; then if the mass of the Earth is known, the mass of the Sun can be calculated from Equation 18. Or, if the mass of the Sun is known, that of the Earth can be calculated.

The mass of the Earth was worked out by a method independent of the harmonic law in 1798. After that, the mass of any astronomical body which is itself at a known distance, and has a body circling it at a known distance and in a known period (all these quantities being easy to determine within the solar system) can quickly be determined. For this reason, the masses of Mars, Jupiter, Saturn, Uranus, and Neptune, all with satellites, are known with considerable accuracy.

The masses of Mercury, Venus, and Pluto, which lack known satellites, can only be worked out by more indirect means and are known with considerably less accuracy. (It seems unreasonable that the mass of Venus is less well known than that of Neptune when the latter is a hundred times farther from us, but now you see why.)

The masses of the various satellites (except for the Moon itself, which is a special case) are hard to determine for similar reasons. The harmonic law can't be used because their masses are drowned by the much larger mass of their primary, and no other method of mass determination is as convenient or as accurate.

Periods, distances, and orbital velocities of satellites, real or imagined, can be worked out for any planet (real or imaginary) for which the mass is known, exactly as these quantities can be worked out for the planets with respect to the Sun.

Without going into arithmetical details, I will list some data in Table 36, on the surface satellite for each planet; the theoretical situation where a satellite just

*Table 36*

| PLANET | | SURFACE SATELLITE | |
| | PERIOD (HOURS) | PERIOD (MINUTES) | ORBITAL VELOCITY (MILES PER SEC.) |
| --- | --- | --- | --- |
| Mercury | 3.13 | 188 | 1.87 |
| Venus | 1.44 | 86½ | 4.58 |
| Earth | 1.41 | 84½ | 4.95 |
| Mars | 1.65 | 99 | 2.27 |
| Jupiter | 2.96 | 177 | 26.4 |
| Saturn | 4.23 | 254 | 15.6 |
| Uranus | 2.62 | 157 | 9.85 |
| Neptune | 2.28 | 137 | 11.2 |
| Sun | 2.73 | 165 | 271 |

skims the planetary equator. For this, use must be made of both mass and radius of the planet and these values are so uncertain in the case of Pluto that I will leave it out. In its place, for comparison purposes, I include the Sun.

If you consider Table 36, you will see that the period of a minimum satellite can be long for either of two reasons. As in the case of Mercury, the planet is light and its gravitational force is so weak that the satellite is moved along slowly and takes several hours to negotiate even the small length of the planetary equator.

On the other hand, as in the case of the Sun or of Jupiter, the gravitational force is great and the surface satellite whizzes along at high speed, but the central body is so large that even at high speed, several hours must elapse before the circuit is completed.

The period of the surface satellite is shortest when the planet packs as much mass as possible into as small a volume as possible. In other words, the greater the density of the central body, the shorter the period of the surface satellite. Since Saturn is the least dense of the bodies listed in Table 36, it is not surprising that its surface satellite has the longest period.

As it happens, of all the sizable bodies of the solar system, our own planet, Earth, is the densest. The period of its surface satellite is therefore the shortest.

An astronaut in orbit about the Earth, a hundred miles or so above the surface, is virtually a surface satellite and he completes his circuit of the earth in just under ninety minutes. An astronaut of no other sizable body in the solar system could perform so speedy a circumnavigation.

How's that for a system-wide distinction for Gagarin, Glenn, and company?

# 16. SQU-U-U-USH!

ANYONE WHO LIKES to slip his imagination off its leash and let it roam freely is bound to find it hunting down extremes with the greatest abandon. At least, it is so in the case of my own imagination (which, at the best of times, is held back only by a rather badly raveled piece of string).

At various times, I have tried to track down the most instantaneous instant, the most infinite infinity, the hottest heat, the coldest cold, and so on. Now I am impelled to track down the densest density into its (as we shall see) rather glamourous lair.

To begin at the beginning, we can consider the substances that exist under ordinary conditions on Earth. As I said in Chapter 9, the densest normal substance is the inert metal osmium.

The density of any substance is the mass of a given volume of that substance under fixed environmental conditions. At ordinary temperatures and pressures a cubic centimeter of osmium has a mass of 22.5 grams. Its density is therefore 22.5 grams per cubic centimeter.

To make use of common units, a cubic inch of osmium has a mass of 13 ounces. Its density, therefore, is also 13 ounces per cubic inch.

This is quite dense. Imagine a brick-shaped object of 2 inches by 4 inches by 8 inches. If it were an ordinary brick, its mass would be in the neighborhood of 4.5 pounds. If it were made of solid, pure osmium, it would

227

weigh about 52 pounds (and be worth about $120,000, though that is neither here nor there).

Suppose, then, that instead of measuring still more extreme densities in grams per cubic centimeter or ounces per cubic inch, we measure it in terms of "osmium units" (a term I have just invented myself and take full responsibility for) and abbreviate that as "o.u." All we need do is remember that 1 o.u. is equal to 13 ounces per cubic inch or 22.5 grams per cubic centimeter and we can easily make the conversion into common units or metric units if we wish.

And the use of o.u. gives us the benefit of a bit of drama. Any material with a density of 2 o.u. is, we see at once, twice as dense as the densest material we can ever encounter under ordinary conditions.

How can we have a material that is denser than the densest substance that exists? Remember that I gave the density of osmium "at ordinary temperatures and pressures" as the "fixed environmental conditions." Since density is the ratio of mass to volume, we can increase density by changing the environmental conditions in such a way as to raise the value of the mass, lower that of the volume, or both.

By setting an object into motion relative to ourselves, we can (Einstein's theory tells us) both increase the mass and decrease the volume. If a 1-inch cube of osmium sped past us at a velocity of 80,000 miles a second, we would find that its length in the direction of light would be reduced to 0.9 inches and its volume, therefore, to 0.9 cubic inches. Its mass would be increased to 14.3 ounces and its density would therefore become 1.22 o.u.

This is not much of an increase in density considering the enormous task of setting a cubic inch of osmium into motion at half the velocity of light. And at all ordinary velocities, the change in mass and volume of any object is negligible. Let's forget velocity, therefore.

228

If we deal with an object at rest, there is no way of increasing the mass, but there are two ways of decreasing the volume. We can lower the temperature or we can raise the pressure.

As far as lowering the temperature is concerned, there is a stern limit set for us—that of absolute zero, which is only about 300 Centigrade degrees below room temperature. Unfortunately, the decrease in volume of solids with drop in temperature is quite small and 300 degrees does little. From the figures available to me. I estimate that a mass of osmium taking up 1 cubic inch at room temperature would take up 0.994 cubic inches at absoulte zero. The density would rise to 1.006 o.u., which is an increase not worth dealing with.

That leaves us with pressure. Physicists have learned to produce pressures in the range of hundreds of tons per square inch. This is enough to distort atomic structure and force atoms to occupy a smaller volume than normal.

Some solids are more compressible than others. For instance, cesium, the most compressible solid available to experimenters, can be squashed down to a volume less than half normal. The most incompressible substance, diamond, can be reduced in volume only by a couple of percent. I have come across no record of osmium itself being put under high pressure, but if we assume that its volume can be reduced by 10 percent, then its density would move up to 1.11 o.u.

Of course, we need not confine ourselves to manmade pressures only. The universe has examples of naturally occurring pressures far higher than anything the laboratory can produce. The center of any sizable astronomic body is under extreme pressure due to its own gravitational field. The center of the Earth, for instance, must bear the gravitationally induced weight of its own vast mass.

One calculation places the pressure at the center of

the Earth at as high as 4,000,000 atmospheres. Since the pressure of 1 atmosphere is 14.7 pounds per square inch, the pressure at the center of the Earth may be as high as 30,000 tons per square inch.

The average density of the Earth as a whole is 0.244 o.u. The density of the rocks on Earth's surface, however, averages at merely about 0.125 o.u. This light crust is balanced by a dense center—not surprisingly, in view of the great central pressures. The density of the material at the very center of the Earth is estimated to be as high as 0.800 o.u.

This is less dense than osmium, but the material at Earth's center is a nickel-iron alloy which, under ordinary conditions, has a density of merely 0.350 o.u. In other words, the material in the Earth's center, though much less compressible than cesium, has been squashed to something more than twice its normal density. If we assume that osmium is about as compressible as nickel-iron, then we might expect a sample of solid osmium to achieve a density of 2.0 o.u. if it were transported intact to the Earth's center.

It so happens that a normal atom is mostly empty space. Roughly speaking, an atom has a diameter of about $10^{-8}$ centimeters, and contains a nucleus (possessing nearly all the mass of the atom) with a diameter of about $10^{-13}$ centimeters.

These nuclei, which are the great contributors to the density of any substance, are held apart at distances at least ten thousand times their own diameter by a thinly spread out organization of electrons (with very little mass) in the outer reaches of the atom.

As pressure increases, the electrons give until finally their organization breaks down altogether. This breakdown of electron organization has been calculated as taking place when pressures of 750,000 tons per square inch are reached. This is a pressure twenty-five times as great as that at the center of the Earth. The pressure at the center of a planet like Jupiter, over three hundred times as massive as the Earth, must approach this figure, so that it is sometimes said that Jupiter is almost the largest chunk of normal matter that can exist.

Once the electron organization collapses through pressure, then neighboring nuclei can approach each other much more closely. A given mass is then confined in a much smaller volume and the density shoots up tremendously. Matter made up of atoms in which the electron organization has broken down is referred to as "degenerate matter."

It would appear that an object must have a mass about ten times that of Jupiter before it reaches central temperatures great enough to ignite thermonuclear reactions and thus becomes a star. A body this large would surely have central pressures great enough to break down the electron organization of atoms. We can suppose, therefore, that any star must have a degenerate core.

Consider the Sun, for instance. It is made up almost entirely of hydrogen and helium, which are the least dense of all the ordinary forms of matter. Solid hydrogen has a density of about 0.03 o.u. while solid helium has a density of about 0.06 o.u.

These solids are solids only at extremely low temperatures, however. At ordinary temperatures and pressures, they are gases, with densities of about 0.000004 and 0.000008 o.u. respectively. At the temperature of the Sun's surface (but at ordinary pressure) the densities would be 0.0000002 and 0.0000004 o.u.; and at the temperature of the Sun's center (but still at ordinary pressure) it would be about 0.0000000001 and 0.0000000002 o.u.

In actual fact, the average density of the Sun is 0.063 o.u. This is not a high density by ordinary standards, being only 1.4 times that of water, but considering the constitution and temperature of the Sun, it is tremendously high; millions of times as high as it "ought" to

231

be. The answer is to be found in the vast pressures that compress the unbelievably hot hydrogen and helium to the point where the electron organization breaks down.

It is estimated that at the center of the Sun, the temperature is about 15,000,000°K., and the density is just about 4 o.u. This central core of the Sun (consisting almost entirely of helium) is the densest material that exists in the solar system.

There is, however, a vast universe outside the solar system. There are stars that consist almost entirely of degenerate matter and that have densities which, even on the average, are considerably higher than the maximum density of the Sun's center. Because they are small, and yet white-hot, they are called "white dwarfs."

Only about one hundred white dwarfs are known altogether. This small number is delusive. White dwarfs are so low in total luminosity that they must be quite close to our solar system to be seen at all. From the number that do exist in our own stellar neighborhood, however, it can be estimated that as many as 3 percent of all stars are white dwarfs—which would mean four billion of them in our own Galaxy alone.

This is not surprising since the white dwarf may well be a terminal stage in the evolution of almost all stars. The brighter the star, the sooner it reaches that terminal. In another five billion years, perhaps, all stars existing today that are brighter than the Sun will have become white dwarfs. (That does not necessarily mean that no bright stars will be left because many more will have come into existence in the meantime.)

The first white dwarf to be discovered, and the best known, is Sirius B, the companion of the bright star Sirius. It has a mass about equal to that of our Sun, but a diameter of about thirty thousand miles, so that it is about the size of the planet Uranus. Its *average* density is about 1,500 o.u. A cubic inch of Sirius B would have a mass of 0.6 tons. Instead of having merely a degenerate core, as the Sun does, Sirius B is nearly all degen-

232

erate, with only a thin outer shell, a few hundred miles thick, of ordinary matter.

Sirius B is, however, rather a mild case of a white dwarf. In general, white dwarfs are more tightly packed and denser than Sirius B. One estimate places the average density of an average white dwarf at about 15,000 o.u., or ten times that of Sirius B. A cubic inch of average white dwarf material would then have a mass of 6 tons.

The smallest white dwarf yet discovered ("Luyton's star," if we wish to use the name of the discoverer) is only 1,700 miles in diameter—less than that of our Moon. It has a volume only $\frac{1}{100}$ that of the Earth, yet it has an estimated mass equal to at least half that of our Sun. Its density would then be about 4,000,000 o.u. and a cubic inch of its material would have a mass of about 1,600 tons.

We are dealing here with large densities indeed, yet we are nowhere near the ultimate squ-u-u-ush.

Suppose we consider Luyton's star in more detail. If it has a mass equal to half that of the Sun, then its mass must be just about $10^{30}$ kilograms. The mass of a nucleon (that is, a proton or a neutron) is about $1.67 \times 10^{-27}$ kilograms, so that Luyton's star must contain about $6 \times 10^{56}$ nucleons.

The diameter of Luyton's star is 1,700 miles or $2.74 \times 10^{8}$ centimeters. The volume of Luyton's star, therefore, comes to $1.08 \times 10^{25}$ cubic centimeters.

If we divide $1.08 \times 10^{25}$ (the volume of the star) by $6 \times 10^{56}$ (the number of its nucleons) we find that each nucleon has, on the average, a space of $1.8 \times 10^{-32}$ cubic centimeters in which to knock about.

This is a tiny space if you look upon it as a hundred-millionth the volume taken up by an ordinary atom here on Earth. Nevertheless, it is about a hundred million times as voluminous as the actual volume of the individual nucleon itself. In other words, even Luyton's star is almost entirely empty space!

To indicate how empty it is, we can say that at any given instant, neighboring nucleons in Luyton's star will be separated by distances of about five hundred times their own diameter. If we built a structure of 1-inch cubes and had each cube placed 42 feet from its neighbor, we would rightly consider our structure to be a very loose one indeed and to consist mostly of empty space.

What keeps a white dwarf from collapsing further than it does? Well, it doesn't consist of nucleons only, but of electrons as well. The electrons are no longer organized as in ordinary atoms but exist as a kind of dense "electron gas." The nucleons could be squashed together and be held together by the strong nuclear force (*see* Chapter 11) but electrons can only repel each other and the closer they are forced together the more strongly they repel each other.

There is then a balance between two opposing forces. There is gravitation (and nuclear force) tending to collapse a white dwarf and a powerful electron repulsion tending to expand it. An equilibrium is reached at a point depending a great deal on the total mass of the star. All things being equal the greater the mass of a white dwarf, the greater the gravitational force compressing it and the smaller it is.

A crucial point is reached at a mass equal to 1.44 times that of the Sun. (This was first pointed out by the Indian-American astronomer Subrahmanyan Chandrasekhar, and is therefore called "Chandrasekhar's limit.") Above that mass, the gravitational force would overcome the greatest possible electron repulsion and a white dwarf as we know it could not exist.

As early as 1934, the Swiss-American astronomer Fritz Zwicky pointed out what might happen if Chandrasekhar's limit were exceeded. Electrons forced against protons (the two are present in equal quantities) would form neutrons. These, added to the neutrons already present, would build up a structure consisting of virtually nothing but neutrons. We would have a "neutron star."

Such a neutron star, unsupported by electron gas, would collapse until all empty space was gone. Much of the star may be blown away in the supernova explosion but in the end a mass the size of the Sun might be packed into a sphere with a diameter of no more than ten miles.

The density of such a neutron star would equal about 50,000,000,000,000 o.u. It would be about 12,500,000 times as dense as Luyton's star, and a cubic inch of the "neutronium" from a neutron star would have a mass of 20,000,000,000 tons. Not bad!

Surrounding the ten-mile-thick neutronium core of such a neutron star there would be (according to some calculations) a shell about half a mile thick made up of ordinary white-dwarf matter, and surrounding that an outermost shell of ordinary matter, about twelve feet thick!

Do such neutron stars actually exist? It is not certain.

One estimate I have seen suggests that so far in the lifetime of our Galaxy one hundred million neutron stars have formed. If that is so, there is an even chance that one such star is within one hundred light-years of us. However, if an object ten miles across were merely to radiate light it could not be seen unless it were very close indeed—say within the solar system.

It could radiate more than light, though. It has been calculated that when a neutron star is first formed, the neutronium core is at a temperature of 5,000,000,000° K and that it takes a thousand years for it to cool to 500,000,000° K. In all this time, the thin layer of ordinary matter around the star has an outer surface that remains at 10,000,000° K and radiates x rays.

This, now, is a different situation. X rays are much more energetic than light and can be much more easily

235

detected in feeble doses. For the first thousand years of its existence, then, a neutron star can be detected. After that its radiation fades into the soft x rays and hard ultraviolet and is lost. Assuming that a neutron star forms each century, on the average, there may be as many as ten neutron stars still in their x-ray infancy and still detectable as "x-ray stars."

Actually, a rocket launched on April 29, 1963, did detect two x-ray sources in the sky—one from the Crab Nebula and one, eight times as intense, from a spot in the constellation of Scorpius.

The Crab Nebula is considered to be the remnant of a supernova, the light of the explosion of which reached us nearly a thousand years ago. Could a neutron star be lurking there?

Well, the Moon occasionally occults the Crab Nebula. If a neutron really exists there, the Moon should move across it in a split second and the x rays should be cut off all at once. If the x rays originate in a source other than a neutron star, that source may be wide indeed and the Moon would cut across it—and cut off the x rays—only gradually.

On July 7, 1964, the Moon crossed the Crab Nebula and a rocket was sent up to take measurements (the x rays won't penetrate the atmosphere and must be detected in space). Alas, the x rays cut off gradually. The x-ray source is about a light-year across and is no neutron star. (What is it instead? Nobody knows.)

What about the Scorpius x-ray star? What about others that have recently been detected? Neutron stars? It looks bad. In early 1965 physicists at C.I.T. recalculated the cooling rate of a neutron star, taking into account the effect of neutrino loss. They decided it would cool off so rapidly that it would radiate x rays for only a matter of weeks. The chance that even a single neutron star was formed in the Galaxy with radiation reaching us in the last couple of weeks is virtually nil.

Let's, however, play around with neutron stars anyway. Whether they actually exist or not, speculation remains legal—and fun.

What about its surface gravity, for instance? We can consider four bodies: the Earth, the Sun, Sirius B, and a neutron star of the type we've just discussed. If we set the surface gravity of the Earth at 1, then the surface gravity of the other bodies can be easily calculated as in Table 37.

*Table 37*

| | SURFACE GRAVITY |
|---|---|
| Earth | 1 |
| Sun | 28 |
| Sirius B | 24,000 |
| Neutron star | 210,000,000,000 |

In the previous chapter, I calculated that a planet moving around the Sun while skimming its surface (a "surface planet") would, if atmospheric resistance were neglected, complete its circuit in 2.73 hours and have an orbital velocity of 271 miles per second.

We can use the same sort of calculation to work out the properties of a surface planet for Sirius B and for a neutron star.

For Sirius B, a planet skimming its surface would complete the circuit of the star in exactly 65 seconds and would have to travel at a velocity of 1,450 miles per second. As for the neutron star, a planet skimming its surface would complete a circuit in $\frac{1}{2500}$ of a second and would have to travel at a rate of 78,500 miles per second.

If a surface planet were to move at a velocity equal to 1.414 times its velocity in a circular orbit, it would escape altogether from the grip of its star. We can therefore calculate the escape velocity from the surface of our four representative bodies, giving that escape velocity both in miles per second and as a fraction of the velocity of light, as in Table 38.

### Table 38

| | ESCAPE VELOCITY | |
| | MILES/SECOND | FRACTION OF LIGHT VELOCITY |
| --- | --- | --- |
| Earth | 7 | 0.000038 |
| Sun | 380 | 0.002 |
| Sirius B | 2,000 | 0.011 |
| Neutron star | 110,000 | 0.59 |

In order for any object, then, to get away from the surface of a neutron star it must be traveling at a velocity equal to about ⅗ that of the velocity of light.

The next question is a natural one. What kind of an object would one have to have for the escape velocity from its surface to equal the speed of light?

Well, even pure neutronium would be insufficient, and since I consider that the ultimate squ-u-u-ush, it seems to me that nothing could bring about such a situation.

But, again, let's pretend. Suppose we can somehow find a body so sternly compressed that even the neutrons of which it is composed are squashed together, forcing the mass of the Sun into a ball four miles across.

The density of such a body would be about 310,000,-000,000,000 o.u., some 6.25 times that of an ordinary neutron star, and a cubic inch of its substance would have a mass of 125,000,000,000 tons. Its surface gravity would be 1,300,000,000,000 times that of the Earth and, again, 6.25 times that of an ordinary neutron star.

A surface planet of such a "superneutron star" would make its circuit at a velocity of 131,000 miles a second and complete that circuit in 1/10,000 of a second. The escape velocity from the surface of such a body would be equal to the velocity of light.

Nothing could escape from the surface of such a

superneutron star. Light photons, neutrinos, gravitons (which carry the gravitational force) all travel at only the speed of light and could not escape.

A superneutron star could not, therefore, affect the rest of the universe in any way. It could give no sign of its existence; neither radiational nor gravitational. It could not lose heat, it could not explode; it could do nothing but remain in perfect stasis.

If we accept Einstein's view of gravitation as representing a geometrical shape of space; so that the fabric of space behaves as though it were curved in the presence of matter, and the more sharply curved the greater the concentration of matter; then a superneutron star is one in which space has curved itself into a complete sphere. The superneutron star has been pinched off into a tiny universe all its own, forever closed and self-sufficient.

For any given mass, the radius of the sphere into which it must be compressed for this to happen is called "Schwarzschild radius" after K. Schwarzschild, a physicist who worried about this sort of thing back in 1916 only a year after Einstein's view of gravitation was published.

Naturally, we could never detect a superneutron star even if it existed, no matter how close it was. Such a superneutron star ought, perhaps, to be considered as not part of our universe and therefore as not located anywhere at all. But even if we could imagine such a star located within the Earth or in a spot partly taken up by our own body, it would mean nothing. The Earth and we ourselves would flow around the object and there would be no way in which we could measure the distortion that would result—and therefore there would be no distortion.

Which should, in these wretched days of continual crises and danger, be a great relief to us all.

# 17. THE PROTON-RECKONER

THERE IS, in my heart, a very warm niche for the mathematician Archimedes.

In fact, if transmigrations of souls were something I believed in, I could only wish that my soul had once inhabited the body of Archimedes, because I feel it would have had a congenial home there.

I'll explain why.

Archimedes was a Greek who lived in Syracuse, Sicily. He was born about 287 B.C. and he died in 212 B.C. His lifetime covered a period during which the great days of Greece (speaking militarily and politically) were long since over, and when Rome was passing through its meteoric rise to world power. In fact, Archimedes died during the looting of Syracuse by the conquering Roman army. The period, however, represents the century during which Greek science reached its height—and Archimedes stands at the pinnacle of Greek science.

But that's not why I feel the particular kinship with him (after all, I stand at no pinnacle of any science). It is rather because of a single work of his; one called "Psammites" in Greek, "Arenarius" in Latin, and "The Sand-Reckoner" in English.

It is addressed to Gelon, the eldest son of the Syracusan king, and it begins as follows:

"There are some, king Gelon, who think that the number of the sand is infinite in multitude; and I mean by the sand not only that which exists about Syracuse and the rest of Sicily but also that which is found in

240

every region whether inhabited or uninhabited. Again there are some who, without regarding it as infinite, yet think that no number has been named which is great enough to exceed its multitude. And it is clear that they who hold this view, if they imagined a mass made up of sand in other respects as large as the mass of the earth, including in it all the seas and the hollows of the earth filled up to a height equal to that of the highest of the mountains, would be many times further still from recognizing that any number could be expressed which exceeded the multitude of the sand so taken. But I will try to show you by means of geometrical proofs, which you will be able to follow, that, of the numbers named by me and given in the work which I sent to Zeuxippus, some exceed not only the number of the mass of sand equal in magnitude to the earth filled up in the way described but also that of a mass equal in magnitude to the universe."

Archimedes then goes on to invent a system for expressing large numbers and follows that system clear up to a number which we would express as $10^{80,000,000,000,000,000}$, or nearly $10^{10^{17}}$.

After that, he sets about estimating the size of the universe according to the best knowledge of his day. He also sets about defining the size of a grain of sand. Ten thousand grains of sand, he says, would be contained in a poppy seed, where the poppy seed is $\frac{1}{40}$ of a finger-breadth in diameter.

Given the size of the universe and the size of a grain of sand, he easily determines how many grains of sand would be required to fill the universe. It works out to a certain figure in his system of numbers, which in *our* system of numbers is equal to $10^{63}$.

It's obvious to me (and I say this with all possible respect) that Archimedes was writing one of my science essays for me, and that is why he has wormed his way into my heart.

But let's see what can be done to advance his article further in as close an approach as possible to the original spirit.

The diameter of a poppy seed, says Archimedes, is ¼₀ of a finger-breadth. My own fingers seem to be about 20 millimeters in diameter and so the diameter of a poppy seed would be, by Archimedes' definition, 0.5 millimeters.

If a sphere 0.5 millimeters in diameter will hold 10,000 ($10^4$) grains of sand and if Archimedes' universe will hold $10^{63}$ grains of sand, then the volume of Archimedes universe is $10^{59}$ times as great as that of a poppy seed. The diameter of the universe would then be $\sqrt[3]{10^{59}}$ times as great as that of a poppy seed. The cube root of $10^{59}$ is equal to $4.65 \times 10^{19}$ and if that is multiplied by 0.5 millimeters, it turns out that Archimedes' universe is $2.3 \times 10^{19}$ millimeters in diameter, or, taking half that value, $1.15 \times 10^{19}$ millimeters in radius.

This radius comes out to 1.2 light-years. In those days, the stars were assumed to be fixed to a large sphere with the Earth at the center, so that Archimedes was saying that the sphere of the fixed stars was about 1.2 light-years from the Earth in every direction.

This is a very respectable figure for an ancient mathematician to arrive at, at a time when the true distance of the very nearest heavenly body—the Moon —was just in the process of being worked out and when all other distances were completely unknown.

Nevertheless, it falls far short of the truth and even the nearest star, as we now know, is nearly four times the distance from us that Archimedes conceived all the stars to be.

What, then, is the real size of the universe?

The objects in the universe which are farthest from us are the galaxies; and some of them are much farther than others. Early in the twentieth century, it was determined that the galaxies (with a very few exceptions among those closest to us) were all receding from us. Furthermore, the dimmer the galaxy and therefore the farther (presumably), the greater the rate of recession.

In 1929, the American astronomer Edwin Powell Hubble decided that, from the data available, it would seem that there was a linear relationship between speed of recession and distance. In other words, if galaxy 1 were twice as far as galaxy 2, then galaxy 1 would be receding from us at twice the velocity that galaxy 2 would be.

This relationship (usually called Hubble's Law) can be expressed as follows:

$$R=kD \qquad \text{(Equation 21)}$$

where $R$ is the speed of recession of a galaxy, $D$ its distance, and $k$ a constant, which we may call "Hubble's constant."

This is not one of the great basic laws of the universe in which scientists can feel complete confidence. However, in the nearly forty years since Hubble's Law was propounded, it does not seem to have misled astronomers and no observational evidence as to its falsity has been advanced. Therefore, it continues to be accepted.

One of the strengths of Hubble's Law is that it is the sort of thing that would indeed be expected if the universe as a whole (but not the matter that made it up) were expanding. In that case, every galaxy would be moving away from every other galaxy and from the vantage point of any one galaxy, the speed of recession of the other galaxies would indeed increase linearly with distance. Since the equations of Einstein's General Theory of Relativity can be made to fit the expanding universe (indeed the Dutch astronomer Willem de Sitter suggested an expanding universe years before Hubble's Law was proposed) astronomers are reasonably happy.

But what is the value of Hubble's constant? The first suggestion was that it was equal to five hundred kilometers per second per million parsecs. That would mean that an object a million parsecs away would be receding from us at a speed of five hundred kilometers per second; an object two million parsecs away at a speed of one thousand kilometers per second; an object three million parsecs away at a speed of fifteen hundred kilometers per second, and so on.

This value of the constant, it turned out, was too high by a considerable amount. Current thinking apparently would make its value somewhere between seventy-five and one hundred and seventy-five kilometers per second per million parsecs. Since the size of the constant has been shrinking as astronomers gain more and more information, I suspect that the lower limit of the current estimate is the most nearly valid value and I will take seventy-five kilometers per second per million parsecs as the value of Hubble's constant.

In that case, how far distant can galaxies exist? If, with every million parsecs, the speed of recession increases by seventy-five kilometers per second, then, eventually, a recession equal to the speed of light (three hundred thousand kilometers per second) will be reached.

And what about galaxies still more distant? If Hubble's Law holds firmly at all distances and if we ignore the laws of relativity, then galaxies still further than those already receding at the speed of light must be viewed as receding at speeds greater than that of light.

We needn't pause here to take up the question as to whether speeds greater than that of light are possible or not, and whether such beyond-the-limit galaxies can exist or not. It doesn't matter. Light from a galaxy receding from us at a speed greater than light cannot reach us; nor can neutrinos nor gravitational influence nor electromagnetic fields nor anything. Such galaxies cannot be observed in any way and therefore, as far as we are concerned, do not exist, whether we argue according to the Gospel of Einstein or the Gospel of Newton.

We have, then, what we call an Observable Universe. This is not merely that portion of the universe which happens to be observable with our best and most powerful instruments; but that portion of the universe which is all that can be observed even with perfect instruments of infinite power.

The Observable Universe, then, is finite in volume and its radius is equal to that distance at which the speed of recession of a galaxy is three hundred thousand kilometers per second.

Suppose we express Equation 21 as

$$D=R/k \qquad \text{(Equation 22)}$$

set $R$ equal to three hundred thousand kilometers per second and $k$ equal to seventy-five kilometers per second per million parsecs. We can then solve for $D$ and the answer will come out in units of million parsecs.

It turns out, then, that

$$D=30,000 \div 75=4,000 \qquad \text{(Equation 23)}$$

The farthest possible distance from us; or, what amounts to the same thing, the radius of the Observable Universe; is 4,000 million parsecs, or 4,000,000,000 parsecs. A parsec is equal to 3.25 light-years, which means that the radius of the Observable Universe is 13,000,000,000 light-years. This can be called the Hubble Radius.

Astronomers have not yet penetrated the full distance of the Hubble Radius, but they are approaching it. From Mount Palomar comes word that the astronomer Maarten Schmidt has determined that an object identified as 3C9 is receding at a speed of 240,000 kilometers per second, four-fifths the speed of light. That object is, therefore, a little more than ten billion light-years distant, and is the most distant object known.

As you see, the radius of the Observable Universe is

245

immensely greater than the radius of Archimedes' universe: thirteen billion as compared to 1.2. The ratio is just about ten billion. If the volumes of two spheres are compared, they vary with the cube of the radii. If the radius of the Observable Universe is $10^{10}$ times that of Archimedes' universe, the volume of the former is $(10^{10})^3$ or $10^{30}$ times that of the latter.

If the number of sand particles that filled Archimedes' universe is $10^{63}$, then the number required to fill the immensely larger volume of the Observable Universe is $10^{93}$.

But, after all, why cling to sand grains? Archimedes simply used them in order to fill the greatest possible volume with the smallest possible objects. Indeed, he stretched things a little. If a poppy seed 0.5 millimeters in diameter will hold ten thousand grains of sand, then each grain of sand must be 0.025 millimeters in diameter. These are pretty fine grains of sand, individually invisible to the eye.

We can do better. We know of atoms, which Archimedes did not, and of subatomic particles, too. Suppose we try to search among such objects for the smallest possible volume; not merely a volume, but the Smallest Possible Volume.

If it were the smallest possible mass we were searching for, there would be no problem; it would be the rest mass of the electron which is $9.1 \times 10^{-28}$ grams. No object that has any mass at all has a smaller mass than the electron. (The positron has a mass that is as small, but the positron is merely the electron's anti-particle, the looking-glass version of the electron, in other words.)

There are particles less massive than the electron. Examples are the photon and the various neutrinos (*see* Chapter 12), but these all have *zero* rest mass, and do not qualify as an "object that has any mass at all."

Why is this? Well, the electron has one other item of uniqueness. It is the least massive object which can carry an electric charge. Particles with zero rest mass are invariably electrically uncharged, so that the existence of electric charge seems to require the presence of mass—and of mass no smaller than that associated with the electron.

Perhaps electric charge *is* mass, and the electron is nothing but electric charge—whatever that is.

Yet it is possible to have a particle such as the proton, which is 1,836 times as massive as the electron, with an electric charge no greater. Or we can have a particle such as a neutron, which is 1,838 times as massive as an electron and has no charge at all.

We might look at such massive, undercharged particles as consisting of numerous charges of both types, positive and negative, most or all of which cancel one another, leaving one positive charge in excess in the case of the proton, and no uncanceled charge at all in the case of the neutron.

But, then, how can charges cancel each other without, at the same time, cancelling the associated mass? No one knows. The answer to such questions may not come before considerably more is learned about the internal structure of protons and neutrons. We will have to wait.

Now what about volume?

We can talk about the mass of subatomic particles with confidence, but volume is another matter. All particles exhibit wave properties, and associated with all chunks of matter are "matter-waves" of wavelength varying inversely with the momentum of the particles (that is, with the product of their mass and velocity).

The matter-waves associated with electrons have wavelengths of the order of $10^{-8}$ centimeters, which is about the diameter of an atom. It is therefore unrealistic to talk about the electron as a particle, or to view it as a hard, shiny sphere with a definite volume. Thanks to its wave nature, the electron "smears out" to fill the atom of which it forms a part. Sometimes it is "smeared out" over a whole group of atoms.

247

Massless particles such as photons and neutrinos are even more noticeably wave-forms in nature and can even less be spoken of as having a volume.

If we move on to a proton, however (or a neutron), we find an object with a mass nearly two thousand times an electron. This means that all other things being equal the wavelength of the matter-wave associated with the proton ought to be about a two-thousandth that associated with the electron.

The matter-waves are drawn in tightly about the proton and its particulate nature is correspondingly enhanced. The proton *can* be thought of as a particle and one *can* speak of it as having a definite volume, one that is much less than the wavelength of the smeared out electron. (To be sure, if a proton could be magnified sufficiently to look at we would find it had a hazy surface with no clear boundary so that its volume would be only approximately "definite.")

Suppose we pass on to objects even more massive than the proton. Would the matter-waves be drawn in still further and the volume be even less? There are subatomic particles more massive than the proton. All are extremely short-lived, however, and I have come across no estimates of their volumes.

Still, we can build up conglomerations of many protons and neutrons which are stable enough to be studied. These are the various atomic nuclei. An atomic nucleus built up of, say, ten protons and ten neutrons would be twenty times as massive as a single proton and the matter-waves associated with the nucleus as a whole would have a wavelength correspondingly shorter. Would this contract the volume of the twenty protons and neutrons to less than that of a single proton?

Apparently not. By the time you reach a body as massive as the proton, its particulate nature is so prominent that it can be treated almost as a tiny billiard ball. No matter how many protons and neutrons are lumped together in an atomic nucleus each individual proton and neutron retains about its original volume. This means that the volume of a proton may well be considered as the smallest volume that has any meaning. That is, you can speak of a volume "half that of a proton" but you will never find anything that will fill that volume without lapping over, either as a particle or a wave.

The size of various atomic nuclei have been calculated. The radius of a carbon nucleus, for instance, has been worked out as $3.8 \times 10^{-13}$ centimeters and that of a bismuth nucleus as about $8 \times 10^{-13}$ centimeters. If a nucleus is made up of a closely packed sphere of incompressible neutrons or protons then the volume of two such spheres ought to be related as the cube roots of the number of particles. The number of particles in a carbon nucleus is 12 (6 protons and 6 neutrons) and the number in a bismuth nucleus is 209 (83 protons and 126 neutrons). The ratio of the number of particles is 209/12 or 17.4 and the cube root of 17.4 is 2.58. Therefore, the radius of the bismuth nucleus should be 2.58 times that of the carbon nucleus and the actual ratio is 2.1. In view of the uncertainties of measurement, this isn't bad.

Let's next compare the carbon nucleus to a single proton (or neutron). The carbon nucleus has twelve particles and the proton but one. The ratio is 12 and the cube root of that is just about 2.3. Therefore, the radius of the carbon nucleus ought to be about 2.3 times the radius of a proton. We find, then, that the radius of a proton is about $1.6 \times 10^{-13}$ centimeters.

Now we can line up protons side by side and see how many will stretch clear across the Observable Universe. If we divide the radius of the Observable Universe by the radius of a proton, we will get the answer.

The radius of the Observable Universe is thirteen billion light-years or $1.3 \times 10^{10}$ light-years, and each light-year is $9.5 \times 10^{17}$ centimeters long. In centimeters then, the radius of the Observable Universe is $1.23 \times 10^{28}$. Divide that by the radius of the proton, which is $1.6 \times 10^{-13}$ centimeters and you have the answer: $7.7 \times 10^{40}$.

In other words, if anyone ever asks you: "How many protons can you line up side by side?" you can answer "77,000,000,000,000,000,000,000,000,000,000,-000,000,000!" because there is no room to line up any more.

Now for volume. If the proton has a radius of $1.6 \times 10^{-13}$ centimeters, and it is assumed to be spherical, it has a volume of $1.7 \times 10^{-40}$ cubic centimeters, and that is the Smallest Possible Volume. Again, given a radius of $1.23 \times 10^{28}$ centimeters for the Observable Universe, its volume is $7.8 \times 10^{84}$ cubic centimeters, and that is the Greatest Possible Volume.

We next suppose that the Greatest Possible Volume is packed perfectly tightly (leaving no empty spaces) with objects of the Smallest Possible Volume. If we divided $7.8 \times 10^{84}$ by $1.7 \times 10^{-40}$, we find that the number of protons it takes to fill the Observable Universe is $4.6 \times 10^{124}$.

That is the solution (by modern standards) of the problem that Archimedes proposed for himself in "The Sand-Reckoner" and, oddly enough, the modern solution is almost exactly the square of Archimedes' solution since $(10^{63})^2 = 10^{126}$.

However, Archimedes need not be abashed at this, wherever he may be along the Great Blackboard in the Sky. He was doing more than merely chopping figures to come up with a large one. He was engaged in demonstrating an important point in mathematics; that a number system can be devised capable of expressing any finite number however large; and this he succeeded perfectly in doing.

Ah, but I'm not quite done. How many protons are there *really* in the Observable Universe?

The "cosmic density"—that is, the quantity of matter in the universe, if all of it were spread out perfectly evenly—has been estimated at figures ranging from $10^{-30}$ to $10^{-29}$ grams per cubic centimeter. This represents a high-grade vacuum which shows that there is practically no matter in the universe. Nevertheless, there are an enormous number of cubic centimeters in the universe and even "practically no matter" mounts up.

The volume of the Observable Universe, as I said, is $7.8 \times 10^{84}$ cubic centimeters and if the cosmic density is equal throughout the universe and not merely in the few billion light-years nearest ourselves, then the total mass contained in the Observable Universe is from $7.8 \times 10^{54}$ grams to $7.8 \times 10^{55}$ grams. Let's hit that in between and say that the mass of the Observable Universe is $3 \times 10^{55}$ grams. Since the mass of our own Milky Way Galaxy is about $3 \times 10^{44}$ grams, there is enough mass in the Observable Universe to make up a hundred billion ($10^{11}$) galaxies like our own.

Virtually all this mass is resident in the nucleons of the Universe, *i.e.*, the protons and neutrons. The mass of the individual proton or neutron is about $1.67 \times 10^{-24}$, which means that there are something like $1.8 \times 10^{79}$ nucleons in the Observable Universe.

As a first approximation we can suppose the universe to be made up of hydrogen and helium only, with ten atoms of the former for each atom of the latter. The nucleus of the hydrogen atom consists of a single proton and the helium atom consists of two protons and two neutrons. In every eleven atoms, then, there are a total of twelve protons and two neutrons. The ratio of protons to neutrons in the universe is therefore six to one or roughly $1.6 \times 10^{79}$ protons and $0.2 \times 10^{79}$ neutrons in the universe. There are thus ten quadrillion times as many protons in the nearly empty Observable Universe as there are sand grains in Archimedes' fully packed universe.

In addition, each proton is associated with an electron,

so that the total number of particles in the Observable Universe (assuming that only protons, neutrons, and electrons exist in significant numbers) is $3.4 \times 10^{79}$.

This proton-reckoning in the Observable Universe ignores relativistic effects. The further away a galaxy is and the more rapidly it recedes from us, the greater the foreshortening it endures because of the Fitzgerald contraction (at least to our own observing eyes).

Suppose a galaxy were at a distance of ten billion light-years and was receding from us at four-fifths the speed of light. Suppose, further, we saw it edge-on so that ordinarily its extreme length in the line of sight would be one hundred thousand light-years. Because of foreshortening, we would observe that length (assuming we could observe it) to be only sixty thousand light-years.

Galaxies still further away would seem even more foreshortened, and as we approached the Hubble Radius of thirteen billion light-years, where the speed of recession approaches the speed of light, that foreshortening would make the thickness of the galaxies in the line of sight approach zero. We have the picture then, of the neighborhood of the Hubble Radius occupied by paper-thin and paper-thinner galaxies. There would be room for an infinite number of them, all crowded up against the Hubble Radius.

Inhabitants of those galaxies would see nothing wrong, of course. They and their neighbors would be normal galaxies and space about them would be nearly empty. But at *their* Hubble Radius there would be an infinite number of paper-thinner galaxies, including our own!

It is possible, then, that within the finite volume of a nearly empty universe, there is—paradoxical though it may sound—an infinite universe after all, with an infinite number of galaxies, an infinite mass, and, to get back to the central point of this article, an infinite number of protons.

Such a picture of an infinite universe in a finite volume does not square with the "big bang" theory of the universe, which presupposes a finite quantity of mass to begin with; but it fits the "continuous creation" universe which needs an infinite universe, however finite the volume.

The weight of observation is inclining astronomers more and more to the "big bang" but I find myself emotionally attracted to the optimistic picture of "continuous creation."

So far we can only penetrate ten billion years into space, but I wait eagerly. Perhaps in my lifetime, we can make the final three billion light-years to the edge of the Observable Universe and get some indication, somehow, of the presence of an infinite number of galaxies there.

But perhaps not. The faster the galaxies recede, the less energy reaches us from them and the harder they are to detect. The paper-thin galaxies may be there— but may be undetectable.

If the results are inconclusive, I will be left with nothing but faith. And my faith is this—that the universe is boundless and without limit and that never, never, never will mankind lack for a frontier to face and conquer.

## Leonard Engel

THE NEW GENETICS      NS27      95¢

A lucid introduction to the revolution in genetics which may alter the nature of our descendants' lives; including a concise account of the Watson-Crick "double helix" discovery

## John Cunningham Lilly

THE MIND OF THE DOLPHIN:
A Nonhuman Intelligence      NS38      95¢

Adventures in a controversial new world of intelligence with a key to understanding alien communications. With a large selection of fascinating photographs

## Alex Comfort

THE NATURE OF HUMAN NATURE
                          W130      $1.25

An original assessment of man's origins and social evolution. "Profoundly important." J. H. Plumb. Foreword by Anthony Burgess

## Isaac Asimov

FACT AND FANCY      W320      $1.25

Intriguing speculations on the possibilities of science, based on the most recent theories. Illustrated with photographs

## Norbert Weiner

THE HUMAN USE OF HUMAN BEINGS:
Cybernetics and Society      QS7      $1.45

A comparison between computer technology and human psychology and a consideration of its uses in a technological society —by the founder of the science of cybernetics

# TODAY'S SIGNIFICANT BOOKS
## ARE DISCUS 🔵 BOOKS

| | | |
|---|---|---|
| *The American Challenge*<br>J. J. Servan-Schreiber | DS27 | $1.65 |
| *America The Raped*<br>Gene Marine | W199 | $1.25 |
| *The Book Of Imaginary Beings*<br>Jorge Luis Borges | QS19 | $1.45 |
| *The Child In The Family*<br>Maria Montessori | W225 | $1.25 |
| *Conversations With Jorge Luis Borges*<br>Richard Burgin | DS15 | $1.65 |
| *Division Street: America*<br>Studs Terkel | J105 | $1.50 |
| *Escape From Freedom*<br>Erich Fromm | DS35 | $1.65 |
| *The Human Use Of Human Beings*<br>Norbert Wiener | QS7 | $1.45 |
| *Thinking About The Unthinkable*<br>Herbert Kahn | DS34 | $1.65 |
| *Towards A Visual Culture*<br>Caleb Gattegno | DS23 | $1.65 |

---

Where better paperbacks are sold, or directly from the publisher. Include 15¢ per book for handling; allow 3 weeks for delivery.

Avon Books, Mail Order Dept.
250 W. 55th Street, New York, N.Y. 10019